YOUNG WALTER SCOTT

BY Elizabeth Janet Gray

"Please, I don't like Mr. Leechman's school in Bristo Street and I'd rather not go there any more. It's a school for bairns and softies. Please, father, couldn't I go to the High School?"

Young Walter Scott, in spite of his lameness, wasn't a "softie," and he early rebelled at any attempt to place him with those who were. You will respect the courage of this lad, who said, "I'll fight anybody my own size, if I can fight mounted." And fight them he did, until his lip began to swell and blood poured from his nose down the front of his yellow waistcoat.

You will be amused at the way young Scott outwitted Davy Douglas, who always seemed to know the answers to Mr. Fraser's questions. Walter Scott had thought about the matter a long time and finally decided that it was the button that did it. Deprived of his button, Davy would be no brighter than the other boys—or so Walter thought, and events proved that he was right.

You will envy Walter and his friends their secret meeting place in the rocks. It was like a little room, with a floor of soft grass and harebells and with high rocks at the back and lower ones in front that hid it from view. The difficulty of reaching it made it all the more desirable.

You will admire Walter Scott's chivalry when he offered to escort a strange young lady home from church under his umbrella when he saw that she had no protection from the pelting rain.

Above all else, you will like this lad—a very human, mischievous boy, but one whose kindliness, quick wit, and courage made him popular with both young and old. This story of Walter Scott may give you a new conception of famous authors who are, after all, very real people.

* * * * * * *

YOUNG WALTER SCOTT

From a portrait of Walter Scott at the age of twelve

Young Walter Scott

by

Elizabeth Janet Gray (Vining)

"A stout heart to a steep brae."
—Scottish saying.

This special edition is published by arrangement
with the publisher of the regular edition,
The Viking Press.

CADMUS BOOKS
E. M. HALE AND COMPANY
Chicago

THIS BOOK IS FOR MORGAN

ACKNOWLEDGMENTS

First and foremost I wish to thank Sir Walter and Lady Maxwell Scott for their kindness to me at Abbotsford and for their great generosity in allowing me to have photographed for the frontispiece the hitherto unpublished portrait of Scott at the age of twelve, painted by an unknown artist at Kelso, which hangs in Lady Maxwell Scott's book-room at Abbotsford.

My thanks also go to the assistants in charge of the Edinburgh Room of the Edinburgh Public Library for their help in making available to me books, newspapers, and maps in that collection.

I should like also to acknowledge the aid I received from a pamphlet by the Reverend J. W. Jack, D.D., of Glenfarg, Perthshire, entitled *Scott's View from the Wicks of Baiglie*.

ELIZABETH JANET GRAY

CONTENTS

YOUNG WALTER SCOTT

"HE DID SURVIVE——"

H E stood with his back to the wall and his lame leg drawn behind him and scowled at his brothers. They were not at all like what he had imagined brothers would be when he lived safely at Sandyknowe with Aunt Jenny and read the ballads and listened to tales by the fireside. Brothers died for each other, they went away to the Crusades when they had the misfortune to love each other's ladies, they shared horses and spears and last crusts. They didn't yell and jeer and point like this pack of loons.

John was the worst. Thomas was younger and Daniel was hardly more than a baby, but John was three years older. And three years bigger and stronger and more than three years better versed in the ways of this Edinburgh life that seemed so rough and cold and confusing after the simple cosy ways of Sandyknowe.

"Why did ye run home?" John was demanding. "A fine help you'll be in the bickers if ye run from the laddies in our own Square."

"I didna run from them!" He shouted the words at them as loud as he could and then was abruptly silent.

Run? How could he run, with his lame leg? He had walked home because there were so many of the George Square laddies, so many staring eyes, because—he felt the blood hot in his face—because they called him a lamiter. "I came home to get a book."

"A book!" John's exasperated voice shrilled high. "Ye don't have to go to school till next week. Ye don't have to go to the High School even then. You're to go to a little, sweet, private school in Bristo Port till you've got used to being away from Aunt Janet. What do ye want with a book now, when you might be playing with the lads in the Square?"

All those eyes. He knew what was going on behind them. Walter Scott, the lamiter. He'll be no good in a fight, and he can't run. What use is he?

Well, they didn't know what he thought of them. They didn't know anything about the ballad of Hardyknute, or the border raids, or Jamie Telfer of the fair Dodhead and Wight Willie of Aikwood. He was suddenly over-whelmed with homesick longing for Sandyknowe, where a fire burned in the farm parlor and he and Aunt Janet read together. Or Prestonpans, where they had been for a holiday, and he and Captain Dalgetty had discussed the campaigns of the American war as man to man. Dalgetty respected his judgment; small use Dalgetty would have for these Edinburgh loons.

"I don't like the George Square laddies!" he shouted. "They're ignorant!"

Robert came sauntering through the room at that moment, his big brother Robert who was a midshipman in the King's navy and wore the King's uniform. Robert could sing and could tell stories, funny and exciting both, of things that happened on the high seas; he could read a ballad so that it swept you off your feet—a great man, Robert, with his sixteen years and his splendid height and his uniform. A little uncertain in the temper. But he would understand how Walter felt.

"What did I hear you say?"

"He said the George Square laddies were ignorant!" Thus, indignantly, Thomas.

"Ignorant!" The scorn in the midshipman's eye and voice made Walter wince. "You young pedant!"

He administered a brotherly cuff and went on, settling the ruffles at his wrist.

"If you want to get on in Edinburgh, my man," said John, preparing to follow, "you won't be setting yourself up to call lads ignorant. Not unless you can ram it into their heads with your fists, and I doubt that Aunt Janet will have taught you much about fighting."

Anne, who had come, as usual, in the trail of Robert, interposed. She was a gentle little girl, pretty, except for the scar at the edge of her fair hair where she had been so badly burned.

"Don't hurt his feelings," she said. "He's new in the house, and he's lame."

Her gentleness hurt more than the boys' roughness. They were trying—dimly Walter realized it through his smart—to teach him something, but she was pitying him.

At Sandyknowe with Aunt Janet he never had thought very much about being lame. It hadn't seemed to mat-

ter. He had had his pony Marian and had ridden everywhere upon her, galloping over the rough places and
down the hills till his grandmother and his aunt had been
frightened by his hardihood.

But here. . . . A wave of bitterness swept over him.
He remembered way back, remembered something that
he almost never thought of. He couldn't have been more
than two years old when it happened, because it was before Aunt Janet had taken him away to the country. He
had been climbing the stile in the Meadows, slowly,
because of his lame leg, and his nursemaid had jerked
his arm and scolded him because he wasn't quick like
his brothers. . . .

His thick brown brows drew together. He felt alone,
helpless, bewildered. Why had he said he disliked the
George Square boys? He liked them. What if they were
ignorant? They could run and fight and have bickers
with the Potterrow lads—and how was a lamiter to
keep up with them?

"Wattie, my lamb!"

He hadn't seen his mother come into the room. A
warmth and a coolness both seemed to come in with her,
the warmth of her heart and the coolness of her serenity,
like a breeze blowing on the swollen, smarting hurt
within him and soothing it.

"Run out, all of you, while the evening is yet light,
every man of you but Wattie, I want him with me. It's
almost bedtime, have your play out while you can. Be
off with you."

She swept them out. Walter's breath came more evenly. He was comfortable with his mother as with no other of these strangers who were his own family. Short, broad, plain, she had that quality his Aunt Janet called "innerliness," and he responded to it gratefully, wholly.

"Come awa' up to my dressing-room while I get ready for supper. Your father will be bringing guests tonight."

Her arm over his shoulder, they paused before a big portrait above the mantel.

"Your great-grandfather," she said. "You're a wee bit like him in looks. You'll have a deal of work to do in living up to him in character. He was a fine man."

"Beardie," murmured Walter. He knew all about his ancestor from Grandmother and Aunt Janet. He had a great brown beard that he had sworn never to cut until the Stuarts were brought back into power; he had bright blue eyes and round red cheeks, and he was tall and straight. "There were more Walter Scotts than him," he went on eagerly as they turned away. "There was Walter Scott, first laird of Raeburn, his father, and Auld Wat of Harden who married the Flower of Yarrow, and the great Sir Walter Scott who rescued Kinmont Willie from Carlisle Castle under the very nose of Lord Scroope."

"Aye, you've a name to be proud of."

She was short enough to be comfortable to walk with. They went up the stairs together with their arms around each other, and he told her the story of Muckle-Mouthed Meg.

"I've got a big mouth myself. Likely I got it from her."

"Very likely you did. Was it the William Scott that was lame that married her in scant preference to the gallows?"

Walter flushed. "I'm not just sure," he said. "Aunt Jenny would know."

Mrs. Scott's dressing-room had a bright little fire in the grate, for the September evening was frosty. The gray twilight twisted mistily against the window; shelves of leather-bound books stood half in shadow along the wall. Mrs. Scott brushed her hair and changed her cap.

"Is there no a ballad or some such thing about William Boltfoot?" she said.

"Aye. I know one verse:

"The Lord and Lady of Harden,
    Betwixt them procreat was a son,
    Called William Boltfoot of Harden—
    He did survive to be a *man*.

"A fearless horseman, I've always heard he was."

"And a dangerous man with his spear, too. His name was known and feared all through the Borders."

"So I've heard," she said thoughtfully. "William Boltfoot." There was silence in the room for a whole minute. "Now, Wattie," Mrs. Scott went on briskly. "It's time for me to be going downstairs. You may read here till your hour for bed. The third book from the end there—no, this end—you'll find *Macbeth* in it. There are some graund witches there for ye."

After she had gone, Walter took the volume from its place and lay down on his stomach on the hearth rug, where the heat from the fire toasted his back and one side of his face and its light fell red on the dim, foxed pages of his book.

William Boltfoot of Harden. A lamiter. . . .

He rolled over on his back, pillowing his head on his hands and cocking his good knee up in the air.

> The Lord and Lady of Harden,
> Betwixt them procreat was a son,
> Called William Boltfoot of Harden—
> He did survive to be a MAN.

BANAMHORAR-CHAT

WALTER was spending part of his Saturday holiday and all of his twopence in the Krames. He had hesitated in front of Mr. Creech's shop at the east end of the Luckenbooths, where the books and the ballads and the penny chapbooks were to be had, but when he heard the sound of voices and laughter from the room upstairs, where men gathered to talk of literature and affairs, he moved shyly away. In the narrow passageway between the Luckenbooths and St. Giles, stuck like birds' nests between the buttresses of the cathedral, were little stands gay with toys and baubles of all kinds, flaunting their gaudy colors in the shadow of the great buildings.

Wattie's hand fluttered over a collection of Dutch toys, lifted a wooden sword, touched a hobby horse and drew back as if it had been burned. Such a childish toy. He hoped nobody had seen him. Crude and wooden as it was, it reminded him of Marian, and he was swept with a gust of homesickness for Sandyknowe that fairly made him dizzy.

"Dinna be wab-wabstering there a' day," said the old

woman behind the counter. "Pit yer mind tae't and set-tle on something."

She looked, he thought, with her long sharp nose that almost met her pointed chin, like a witch about to drop a rat into the caldron. It was strange that anybody who had such delightful things to sell should be so cross and snippy. Almost without meaning to, he bought a baby for Anne—a wooden baby with arms that moved. Anne had cried that morning because her baby was lost, and the memory of Anne crying made him feel hurt and uncomfortable inside—Anne with the red scar under her fair hair, Anne with the sweet, wistful little face, Anne who lived apart in a world of her own. He would like to see her face light up when she saw the new baby.

When he came around the corner between the ca-thedral and the Tolbooth, the great bell of St. Giles began to ring, deep crashing notes that pressed against your ears and thrilled up from the ground through your feet. Immediately the door of the Parliament House opened and judges and lawyers in gown and wig began to cross the Close to John's Coffee-house for their meridian, walking along in sober procession for all the world like a line of ducks threading their way through a farmyard cluttered with hens. Wattie saw his own fa-ther pass, dignified and quiet and serious-looking, but handsome, too. He walked straight; he didn't waddle, like one, or shuffle his feet, like another; his mouth was not sunken and toothless like Lord Monboddo's, nor did his eyes swim in deep pouches like Lord Braxfield's. Wattie lingered near the statue of Charles II in the center of the Close, ready to wave if his father should turn and recognize him, but Mr. Scott went on into the coffee-house without looking back.

"Awa' wi' ye, awa' wi' ye. The Parliament Close is nae place for laddies!"

One of the Town Guard was bearing down on him, an irritable old Highlander in cocked hat and red uniform, waving his Lochaber ax and making toothless grimaces. Wattie scrambled away hastily and plunged down the Back Stairs, a steep flight of steps leading from the Parliament Close to the Cowgate down below. He might just as well go home now anyhow, he thought. He could give Anne her doll-baby, and he wanted to see the Countess of Sutherland go out for her ride.

George Square was at the very southernmost edge of town. Shortly after Walter was born Mr. Scott had moved his family there from the more convenient but unhealthy, crowded College Wynd, where six babies had died in close succession. The air, as Walter left the high, close-piled city behind him and came out into the open places, grew fresher by the minute. Before him he could see the Pentland Hills lifting their heather-clad shoulders into the sky. They were not so fine as the Eildon Hills from Sandyknowe, but they were hills, windswept and heather-sweet, and he loved to look at them.

At the entrance to George Square he met John and Thomas and Geordie Milne.

"Here he is! Here's Wattie."

They were looking for him! Well!

"Whaur's yer tuppence?"

Oh.

"We're going to get a banner for us George Square lads to have for the bickers, and we need your tuppence."

They hadn't really been looking for *him* at all. And his tuppence was gone.

"I gave *my* penny, Wattie."

He could see in their faces that they were taking his confusion for unwillingness. "I—I spent it," he said with difficulty.

"Ye spent it? What for?"

He went cold all over. If they should find out that he had spent it for a doll-baby! He felt as if his pocket were transparent and that in an instant their accusing eyes must see that dolly.

"I'll no tell."

John was gathering himself together. "Ye went off by yoursel', without consulting anybody, and ye spent your tuppence," he said with profound disgust. "Ye *can't* fight and ye *won't* give your money for the banner—ye won't even tell what was the fine giftie ye bought your-sel'——" He stopped. He glared at Walter and Walter glared back.

"If ye wanted my tuppence why didn't ye tell me ahead of time? I'd have given it to you. But now I've spent it. It's my money and I don't have to tell you what I spent it on——"

"Oh, come away, don't let's waste any more time."

They were gone, with Thomas swaggering along in the wake of the older boys, wagging his curly head and throwing out his chest the way they did. Almost as soon as they had disappeared around the corner into Bristo Street, Walter heard howls and jeers and knew that they were already caught up in the whirl of a bicker.

He limped home, feeling thoroughly ill-treated. He found Anne and gave her the baby without looking to see whether her face lighted up or not. Still hot and sore at heart, he stumped out into the garden in the center of the Square and sat down on a flat stone where he had a good view of Lady Alva's house.

Everything would have been different at Sandyknowe. Grandmother and Uncle Thomas would have had something to say about the way John and Thomas acted, and as for Aunt Jenny—well, her blood wouldn't have sat down with it at all. He had other friends there, too, Sandy Ormiston, the cow-bailie, and the shepherd outdoors, and Tibby Hunter in the house. They would have settled that Geordie Milne. But here. . . . He hated it here. If it weren't for his mother he couldn't endure another minute of it. And she was always busy. He was only one of six for her—five, now that Robert had gone back to his ship—whereas at Sandyknowe he had been the only one.

The noise of horses' hoofs and the light grinding of wheels sounded through the quiet square. Walter stood up. Lady Elizabeth would be taking her ride now.

Lady Elizabeth was a great person in his Edinburgh world. A countess in her own right from the time that her father and mother died within a week of each other when she was scarcely more than a year old, she owned a house and lands far away in the North, and a house in

George Square; she had at twelve raised her own company of Sutherland Fencibles and still reviewed them occasionally in the Square—Walter had seen her do it—and now at fourteen she was a beautiful young lady, and went out riding every afternoon on a black horse with her anxious grandmother following close behind her in a chaise.

The door opened and she came prancing deliciously down the gray stone steps of the gray stone house, a slender and spirited little figure in a hunter's-green riding joseph, with a velvet hat with a plume perched on the side of her curly red-brown hair. The groom made a step out of his hands and she went up into the saddle like a bird; her horse reared just for the fun of it, and his hoofs grated on the cobblestones. Down the steps in her turn, hoop-skirted and monumental, came Lady Alva with two maids in her train bearing shawls and wraps. She was packed into the chaise with all ceremony, and the procession was about to start forth when Lady Elizabeth caught sight of Walter standing in the shrubbery at the edge of the garden. She beckoned to him, and he limped forward eagerly.

"Would you like to ride in the chaise with Grandmamma?"

"I would like it fine, if it wouldn't put Lady Alva out," said Walter with formal politeness. He felt joy bubbling up all through him, melting away the stiff heavy mask that had been over his face all day. This was better, he thought, climbing into the carriage, than trying to keep up with John and Thomas.

He and Lady Alva found a great many things to talk about besides their mutual admiration for the young Countess, so many that afterwards, when pressed for details of the conversation, Walter quite forgot that he had mentioned in passing the need of the George Square lads for a banner. Accordingly, it was as much of a surprise to him as to the other lads when Lady Elizabeth made it known that she herself would give a banner to the cause.

The ceremony of presentation took place late one afternoon when all the lads were home from school and the sun was just going down beyond the Corstorphine hills, the twilight chill creeping out of the shadows in the Meadows. Neil Mackenzie, the tallest of the lads and the best fighter, was to receive it, the others drawn up in drill formation behind him, with the little ones like Thomas Scott and the youngest Gordon boy at the tail end of the line. Walter went back to get his mother. She had promised to come out to see it, but the company had marched around the Square twice and was now halted before the Countess's house. The Countess's domestics were all out in the area, giggling and whispering and peeking through the railing, and it was expected each moment that Lady Elizabeth would come forth with the banner—and still Mrs. Scott had not appeared. So Walter went back for her, hurrying as fast as his dragging leg would let him. At the door he met her.

"Oh, puir laddie, did ye think I had forgotten? It was the man with the coals——"

"I knew you wouldn't mean to forget—— There she comes now. Oh, Mother, look, it's on a standard!"

"Run ahead, you, dinna wait for——" The broken end of her sentence cracked on both their hearts. Mrs. Scott bit her lips, and her arm tightened over Wattie's shoulder. He knew she was grieving for the slip her tongue had made, and he tried to reassure her.

"We'll get a better view from here than if I was in the line," he said stoutly.

Lady Elizabeth stood on her front steps with the banner in her hand. Neil Mackenzie stood at attention in the street with his men behind him. What were they waiting for? Suddenly all heads turned his way and half a dozen arms gestured urgently to Walter.

"Walter Scott. Fetch young Walter Scott."

Thomas came running. "Wattie, Lady Elizabeth wants ye!"

His heart swelling with amazement and joy, Wattie made his way to the foot of the steps, out in front of everybody, Neil and John and Geordie and the Gordon lads. He felt Lady Elizabeth's light firm grasp on his shoulder, looking up he saw the sweet curve of her lips, the smile in her big eyes, the pointed way her hair grew on her forehead, he saw the scarlet-and-white banner hanging from its staff.

"I needed a page boy," she told him. "Stand here by me."

She raised her voice. "Lads of George Square!" she cried. "I give you this banner, to carry against the enemy, to defend with your lives, to guard against dishonor, to—to defend always."

She put the standard into Walter's hands and he carried it to Neil Mackenzie. It was the proudest moment of his life.

"Lady Elizabeth," began Neil, but his voice was so husky that he had to clear his throat and start again: "Most honored patroness, we receive this banner with gratitude and reverence and we swear never to let it drag in the dust or let the Potterrow loons get it, and we thank ye for this beautiful banner——" His sentence ending in breath, he waved the banner vigorously and his troops cheered.

Even in his exalted state Walter could not help noticing that neither of these speeches was as good as the occasion called for. Of course, Lady Elizabeth was a girl; girls weren't expected to make good speeches—and even so, hers was better than Neil's. I could have done it right, thought Wattie; I could have made them a speech.

The cheering stopped and nobody seemed to know what to do next.

"Three more huzzas for Banamhorar-Chat!" cried Walter shrilly.

Though they had no idea what the words might mean, the lads were willing to go on cheering as long as there was a croak in their throats. The servants in the area joined in this one, wagging their heads at each other, and Lady Elizabeth laughed and blushed her pleasure before she waved her hand to the lads and vanished into the house.

The George Square company proceeded to work off steam by marching round the Square with their banner. Walter tried to follow them but they went too fast for him. They had forgotten that he had been page boy; forgotten that if it hadn't been for Walter Scott they wouldn't have had any banner at all.

Walter and his mother walked back to the house together. It was almost dark now; lights were showing in the windows of the gray stone houses, the Pentland Hills beyond the Meadows were a deep purple.

"What did that mean, Wattie, 'Banamhorar-Chat'? It seemed to please the Countess."

"It's her title in Gaelic, the Great Lady of the Cat," he answered lifelessly. "There's a black cat in the Sutherland coat of arms, because in the olden days there were so many wild cats in the lands of Sutherland and Caithness."

"Wherever did ye pick up that bit of knowledge?"

"Lady Alva told me."

"Did she now? She told me that you had told her several things she didn't know before, too."

They had reached their own front door and Wattie stood aside to let his mother go in first. She paused, looking down at him, half proud and half troubled; then she shook her head. "I doubt ye've been overmuch with grown folks, Wattie, it makes it harder for you to get on with the lads."

He frowned and drew down his long upper lip between his teeth. "I like grown folks better," he said. Even in his own ears his voice sounded hollow.

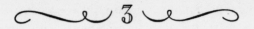

"YOU HAVE HEARD O'
PAUL JONES?"

THE High School lads were coming home. You could hear them shouting in Bristo Street. Walter, who had got out of his school an hour earlier, jumped up from Lady Elizabeth's front steps, where he had been sitting looking at the dark slope of Arthur's Seat against the gray sky and hoping that the Countess would come home soon from her ride.

The din increased—thudding feet and shrill shouts, something about the "enemy" and ships in the Firth. Wattie limped to the corner of the street. Geordie Milne was ahead, his elbows crooked and his red cheeks shaking in time to his pounding steps. John followed close behind waving his arms, and after him the Gordon boys puffing and blowing and bright-eyed with excitement.

"Clear the way," panted Geordie, swerving around Walter. "Important news—Paul Jones bearing down on Leith——"

A yell arose behind them, and John went sprawling on his face, brought down by a great clod of earth that

caught him between the shoulders. At once the air was
full of clods and sticks and even stones. The Potterrow
boys were after them.

The George Square lads turned, their news forgotten.
A bicker came first. John was up in a second. He stooped,
picked up something, let fly with his right arm—and
the very same clod that had laid him low took a Potterrow lad full in the chest. Donald M'Tavish, the bare-
footed, tousle-headed son of Big Donald the Highland
chairman, staggered, winded for the moment, then broke
into a shrill torrent of Gaelic.

George Square made a rush, and all the Potterrow
missiles returned to the Potterrow. Inch by inch at first
the enemy retreated, then broke into a run, the Gordons
and Geordie and John in hot pursuit, backed up by
Jamie Stewart and Rob Campbell from Crichton Street.
Wattie hesitated, and then, with sudden resolution, made
off after them as fast as he could go with his stiff leg.

By the time he caught up with the rest, the Potterrow
loons had reinforcements, and the George Square lads
were retreating.

Donald M'Tavish caught sight of Walter. "Rin, lads,
rin!" he shouted derisively. "Here's a wee lamiter come
to frichten us!"

Wattie flushed angrily. "I'll show him if I'm a lamiter,"
he muttered.

The clod he flung hit no one, but it did him a lot of
good. He stumped on again in a glow. By jing, he was in
a bicker like anybody else.

Once again he was left behind. Behind the Potterrow

loons and far behind the George Square lads who, out-
numbered, were running for home for all they were
worth. They were chased all the way back into the Square
and only saved from being driven into their houses by
the appearance of several older brothers and an array
of men servants, before whom the victors fell back,
jeering.

John came back for Walter. The tape at his knees had
come untied and his breeches hung untidily down his
calves; there was mud on his green waistcoat, and blood
on his coatsleeve where he had wiped his streaming nose.
He put his arm around Wattie's neck.

"They were too many for us. We'll get them next time.
Man, it was a good thing we hadn't our banner with us!"

His heavy arm made going difficult for the lame lad;
he wriggled a bit to shift it to a more comfortable position.

"I suppose you'll tell at home you've been in a bicker,"
said John after a pause, removing his arm. Walter felt
chilled. He wanted to tell. Especially he wanted to tell
his mother. But perhaps John would be blamed.

"I'll no tell," he said a little forlornly. *Telling* reminded him of something that the bicker had chased out
of his mind. "What about Paul Jones?"

"Oh, I almost forgot. Man, we'd better hurry. There's
a squadron of three ships coming up the Firth. They've
got two prizes with them they took off North Berwick,
and 'tis said the pirate Paul Jones is in command and is
to attack Leith."

Paul Jones! He was on everybody's tongue, the rene-

gade Scotsman who had gone over to the Americans and
had been ravaging the coast of Ireland and Scotland for
these six weeks back—the first invader on British soil
since the Normans. There was a song about him. Robert
had sung it when he was at home.

> You have heard o' Paul Jones?
> Have you not? Have you not?
> And you've heard o' Paul Jones?
> Have you not?

He hummed it uncertainly; he could hear the tune in
his mind as Robert had sung it, but he couldn't make it
sound the same himself.

"Will they be warships, John?"

"Aye. There's a ship of fifty guns, they say, and a
frigate of twenty, and a brig of ten."

A little shiver ran down Walter's spine. "What's to
keep them from blowing Leith to pieces and then coming their ways up to Edinburgh?"

"That's just it. A lad told a lad in the Rector's class
that folk in Leith are burying their plate and their
money."

The dull September dusk had closed in. Wind rustled
in the bushes in the Square garden and the air was fresh
and damp and chill in the nostrils. When the boys reached
the front door at Number 25 they learned at once, in
the confusion of lights and voices and figures, that the
news of the invader had got there ahead of them. Mr.
and Mrs. Scott were talking with Mr. Alaster Stewart
of Invernahyle, who stood in the drawing-room doorway

in the attitude of one who has been for some time on the point of leaving. A client of Mr. Scott's, and a great friend of Walter's, he was an old gentleman who in his youth had fought a duel with Rob Roy, had been out in the '45 and had lain hidden for days in a cave after the battle of Culloden Moor. He had promised Wattie a Lochaber ax for his own.

Walter fell on him now with cries of joy, but quickly silenced by a head shake from his mother and a curt "That will do, Walter," from his father, he fell back with Tom and Anne among the shadows. It was clear that Invernahyle had more important things on his mind than even Lochaber axes.

"As I was just saying, the whole town's mad with panic. Down there in Leith they've dragged out three cannons that have been rusting in the Navy Yard these past ten years and set them up on the parapet——"

" 'Tis likely they'll do more harm to anyone who tries to set them off than they could possibly do the enemy," ventured Mrs. Scott.

"Exactly, madam, exactly so. And then, say all these folk who are frightened out of their wits, these pirates and Americans and renegades will set fire to Leith and march up to Edinburgh. And they're fair running about wringing their hands in terror. There's nothing to be afraid of, in a town like this of steep streets and narrow wynds. Give me a handful of Highlanders and I'll guarantee to stop in their tracks any force that the fellow Paul Jones can muster."

His keen old eyes flashed under the thick gray brows.

His whole slender body was taut with the force of his idea.

"I believe you could, sir, I believe you could indeed," said Mr. Scott in a slightly absent voice as if he had said it before.

"I'd rejoice, *rejoice,* sir, in the prospect of drawing my claymore once again in defense of Scotland."

Here Mrs. Scott's attention wandered to John, who was looking cross-eyed at his swollen nose.

"Tuts," she said disapprovingly, "fighting again."

At this Invernahyle looked startled, as if he thought that the rebuke was addressed to him, and Walter and Thomas were obliged to retire under the stairs to laugh.

"Did ye see his face?" moaned Thomas, rolling on his back and clasping his stomach.

"Oh, tuts, Invernahyle, fighting again," said Walter primly, and Thomas squealed faintly and jerked one foot as an indication that he could stand no more.

"I really must be off this time. Wattie—where did the lad go?—well, tell him anyhow that I have a whinger for him and I'll bring it with the ax, certain, next time I come."

He was gone by the time that Wattie had scrambled out, eager to declare himself in favor of the whinger. Walter devoted considerable time and thought that evening to the place where he was going to keep these treasures when he got them, and decided that until he should have a room of his own where he could have a real museum, under the bed was as good a place as any. It was too bad, though. that Invernahyle hadn't brought them with him today, for with Paul Jones at the door and possible fighting in the streets in prospect, it looked as if he might really get a chance to use them.

I've been in a bicker, anyhow, said Wattie to himself.

WHEN THE WIND ROSE

IN spite of the fears of the populace and the secret
hopes of the Scott boys, the night passed without an
invasion. The next morning, when Walter looked out of
his back window, was clear and bright, but the Pentland
Hills were dark against the sky and a rising wind was
busy in the trees in the Meadows. Over to the right the
Castle mounted into the air, its rock gilded by the early
sunshine. From the Castle, Walter thought, on a clear
day like this you could see the Firth all the way to the
Bass Rock and any alien ships that might be sailing on it.
If they stormed Leith, you would see them do it. That
is, if you weren't in school. Wattie thought of Mr. Leechman's private school with sudden loathing. Only babies
went there anyhow, except for one great gowk of a lad
who was simple-minded.

He was busy with a plan when he and Tom and Daniel
started off together a little before eight. As usual John
had gone ahead. It was beneath his dignity to walk with
the younger boys. But to Walter's surprise he joined
them at the corner and without saying anything walked
along beside him, fitting his pace to Walter's slower

one, while Tom and Daniel pranced along ahead, butting and kicking at each other in high spirits.

At the entrance to the school, "In you go," said John, jerking his head toward the door.

Walter's heart thudded. Now was his moment. "In you go," he repeated, copying John's tone. "I thought," he added casually, in an aside to John, "that I'd just step up to the Castle and see could I get a glimpse of Paul Jones."

"Just my idea," said John. "Ye might go along with me, if you think you can keep up."

Walter understood now that John had come back for him, and deep down within him a little hard tightness loosened.

They left Tom gaping. "You'll catch it," he shrilled after them, "if you don't go to school."

John shrugged his shoulders. Floggings were a commonplace in the High School, where a false quantity in a Latin word was good for a beating any day in the week. He looked sideways at Wattie.

"Go back if you want to," he said. "I don't suppose Aunt Janet ever let anybody lay a finger on you."

Walter shook his head and said nothing; he was saving his breath for the struggle of keeping up with John. It was a stiff climb up the steep wynd and he didn't want to ask John to go slower.

Without comment they avoided the region of Parliament Close and turned instead up the Lawnmarket toward the Castle. Wattie wrinkled his nose at the foul smells of refuse and sewage that wandered out of the closes and rose from the street and lurked along the house-walls. An eggshell that the scavengers had missed crunched under his foot.

All the town was excited about the Paul Jones raid. Water caddies stood talking of it while the kegs on their backs slopped over and dribbled down the street. A barber's boy carrying home a retrimmed wig told a serving-maid who had stuck her head out of a window above him,

"——saw him through a spy-glass, hinny. Wearing an American uniform wi' a Glengarry bunnit wi' a wee gold band on it——"

Out on the Castle Walk the wind caught the boys in a great cold blast and all but blew them off the rock. Walter gasped. A lock of hair broke loose from his pigtail and whipped across his face. He took off his hat and held it against his chest. "If it keeps on like this," he shouted, "it'll blow the ships away."

They were not the only ones who had thought to come up here to see the enemy. The wall along the northern side of the Castle Walk was lined with people, pointing, gesticulating, shouting to each other above the wind. John and Wattie soon found a place to squeeze into.

A world in miniature lay spread out below them, the canal, the raw streets and scattered houses of the New Town, the roofs and chimneys of Leith, the Firth of Forth, colorless as pewter, and on it, like toy boats, the sails of the enemy squadron.

"I see five—no, six. One on the other side of the wee church spire yonder."

"Three of them are American," said a man beside Walter. "The two wee ones are prizes, and the cutter yonder will have gone out to reconnoiter, likely. It wasna there when I first came."

"What are they doing? Aren't they going to do anything?"

"They're trying to beat up into Leith Roads, but the wind's against them. If it wad juist blaw haird now, it wad blaw them doon the Firth again, comin' frae the sou'west as it is."

The sun had disappeared. Arthur's Seat towered up in a gray sky above the black ramparts of Salisbury Crags, and far away to the east sky met water in a gray haze at the mouth of the Firth. A storm was coming. If it just came soon enough!

"The cryin' shame of it as I see it," expounded a man on the other side of John, "is this: here this pirate's been on our coasts for five weeks taking our ships and no force has been sent against him. The people of Scotland have shown their loyalty by raising men and money and supporting government and yet they're not trusted with arms. I maintain, sir, with the enemy on our very doorstep, we shall be obliged to take up arms to defend ourselves, our families, and our properties!"

He had all the eloquence of usquebaugh, and he did not even notice when his audience deserted him. Walter and John heard him still holding forth behind them as they made their way up to the Low Battery.

A couple of High School lads joined them. It was colder now and grayer and the wind howled around the

corners of the buildings. The boys avoided the red-coated
sentry and found themselves a lookout. There was as a
matter of fact nothing very much to see, for the six ships
bobbing about in the Firth were so tiny in the distance
that no action was visible on their decks. None of the
boys, however, entertained for an instant the thought
of going back to school. John and George Abercrombie
and Wullie Edmonstone hung over the Castle Wall and
debated the possibility of climbing the Kittle Nine steps
from here, while Walter sat off a bit by himself and
wished that he went to the High School too, instead of
that fusionless little establishment in Bristo Street.

He was conscious of the Castle at his back, above him,
beneath him, around him, a bulk of history supporting
him and crushing him down. These old gray stones had
known Mary Stuart; Argyle had been in prison there;
the Black Dinner had been served to the accompaniment
of clashing arms and the cries of betrayed boys; on the
other side of the rock a man—a Douglas—had let himself down at night by a rope pieced out with knotted
sheets and at the bottom picked up his wounded servant
and carried him on his back to safety. It was all mixed
up in his mind, incident on tragic incident, as though
it had all happened at once. Aunt Jenny had told him
most of the stories, and he had never sorted out the
centuries.

The other lads were off somewhere, climbing. He could
hear their shouts now and again, whirled about and
broken by the wind. A drop of rain fell, and another.

Suddenly it came—sheets of rain driven by a gale. A

slate was wrenched off the roof of the barracks and
splintered on the cobblestones. Rain swept like a curtain before the Castle, and Leith, the Firth, ships and all,
disappeared. It rushed down the Castle Hill, driving people before it, sweeping them away into doorways and
wynds and closes. It sluiced into every corner and within
a few moments was pouring down all the slopes in rivu-
lets and washes and floods. And above all the wind,
howling, banged shutters and whacked people up against
walls, carried away hats, and lashed the pelting rain
furiously against anything that was strong enough to re-
sist.

The boys, drenched to the skin in the first five minutes,
huddled in the shelter of the gateway. Now that something was happening, they were once again excited about
the Paul Jones squadron.

"This will drive them away," they exulted. "They'll
be lucky if it doesn't blow them clear up on the shores
of Fife."

They speculated on how many would sink, and once
when the curtain of rain lifted for a few minutes they
went out into the wet again to count the ships in the
Firth, and could see now only four boats and those scattered.

It grew later and colder, and they grew wetter and
hungrier.

"Well, lads," said John, planting his foot down hard
on the cobblestones and listening with satisfaction to the
sound of water squelching out of his boot, "I think it's
time to go home."

Nobody was out on the streets who did not have to be there. They trotted along close to the walls with their shoulders hunched. The rain beat down on their heads, beat up from the street in a kind of mist in their faces. At the West Bow, John and Walter parted from the other two lads, who lived in the High Street, and turned to the right down the steep hill. There was a roaring flood in the Cowgate; they waded through it and plodded up the Candlemaker Row. Will Sampson's livery stable was flooded and the smell of horses and straw hung heavy over the street. It was hard going for Walter. It was slippery underfoot and his lame leg felt as if it were made of stone.

John slowed down and gave him his arm, which helped quite a bit. Greyfriars Kirkyard was behind them. Heriot's Hospital lay over their right shoulder; their feet were on the Meadow Walk. George Square at last.

Their mother met them in the hall.

"Mercy on us!" she cried.

They stood before her, shivering. Their hair was plastered down on their heads in rat tails; water trickled off the ends of their noses, their chins, the edges of their sleeves, and the tips of their fingers. Pools gathered on the floor about their feet. Walter put out his tongue and licked the soft, tasteless rainwater off his lips.

"Tuts! Dripping like water kelpies, both of you. Upstairs with you and take off every stitch you have on and put on dry clothes from the skin out. And then your father wants to see you in his office."

Ominous words. They dried themselves very thoroughly before the fire in John's room and dressed with meticulous care, wrung out separately each wet garment and hung it before the fire to dry. They were still arranging their damp clothes in even neater and more careful ways when James Wilkinson came to the door to remind them that their father was waiting for them in his office.

"I expect you'll get off for being lame," said John gloomily, "but I shan't."

"No, I won't either. I'll take whatever you get."

This noble pronouncement, however, Walter was not obliged to fulfill—considerably to his relief, especially as the mere saying of it seemed to have sent him up in John's estimation. They both escaped with a lecture. Even the most conscientious parent has to make an exception when Paul Jones is in the Firth.

Mr. Scott sat behind his desk, and the boys stood in front of it. He had a good deal to say, and his stern blue eyes never wavered from them while he said it. Walter, meeting his glance squarely, was soon paying more attention to his father's face than to his words. He had never really looked at his father before.

For all his sternness, he looked kind and faintly puzzled, sitting there half in shadow with the candlelight on his face and on the white ruffles at his throat and wrists, saying in his serious formal way things about duty and opportunity and responsibility that sounded no answering note in his two sons who stood before him, respectful and still very much relieved. But if his father's words said nothing to Walter, something that his father was, did. Quite clearly and abruptly the boy knew that he *liked* his father and that he wanted very much to please him.

"Have you anything to say for yourself, John?"

"No, sir."

"Walter?"

"Yes, sir." He drew a long breath and used it all up in one hasty sentence. "Please, I don't like Mr. Leechman's school in Bristo Street and I'd rather not go there any more. It's a school for bairns and softies."

"It's been well spoken of by those who are in a position to know. Do you think that a lad who takes it upon himself to play truant when the whim strikes him is any kind of judge?"

"No, sir. But it's a fusionless kind o' a place. Nobody ever finishes anything there. Please, father, couldn't I go to the High School?"

"Humph." Mr. Scott slipped his forefinger up under his wig and scratched his temple thoughtfully. "Well, lad, I'll think it over. Perhaps a tutor for a time—— Your good friend Mrs. Cockburn is in the drawing-room with your mother; she's been asking for you both. You'd better go along now and pay your respects to her."

The ladies were about to have tea in front of a sea-coal fire. Mrs. Cockburn stretched out both hands to her favorite, Walter.

"Well, and how's my virtuoso?" she cried.

It was an old joke between them that traced back to the day of their first meeting when Walter had confided to his Aunt Jenny that he thought the author of

the "Flowers of the Forest" was "a virtuoso like myself."
The boys had teased him so much about it that he felt
the blood flame in his face as he limped over to Mrs.
Cockburn to shake hands and be kissed. He was very
fond of the heartsome old lady whose hair at seventy was
as auburn still under her black lace scarf as it had ever
been and whose smile was as blithe as a girl's. She had
bright black eyes, a nose a little like Queen Elizabeth's,
and a pawky underlip; she wore puffed sleeves in a style
peculiarly her own; and she had written, many years ago,
that lovely version of the "Flowers of the Forest" that
begins:

> I've seen the smiling
> Of fortune beguiling——

"So you went to the Castle to see Paul Jones routed.
Sit you down and I'll tell you how that wind happened to
come up so fortuitously."

The boys made themselves useful handing tea and
scones while she talked.

"It was the Secession minister at Kirkaldy did it.
Kirsty, my maid, had the story from her brother not an
hour ago. Mr. Sherriff is his name. He took his chair
down to the water's edge early this morning and he addressed the Lord. 'Now, deer Lord,' he says, 'dinna ye
think it a shame for ye to send this vile piret to rob our
folk o' Kirkaldy, for ye ken they're puir enew a'ready
and hae naething tae spare. The way the ween blaws he'll
be here in a jiffie and wha kens what he may do?' There
was more in that vein, but the upshot of it was, 'I hae

been lang a faithful servant to ye, Lord, but gin ye dinna turn the ween about and blaw the scoundrel out o' our gate I'll nae staur a fit but will juist sit here till the tide comes and droons me. Sae tak' yer will o't.' "

"And then the wind changed?"

"And then the wind changed." Mrs. Cockburn gave a little nod and had another dish of tea. "Mr. Sherriff is very modest about it—he says he only prayed, but the Lord sent the wind."

"We can feel very calm now they're gone," sighed Mrs. Scott, "but we sang anither tune last night when they were coming in the other direction. I'm glad one of the prizes went to the bottom—a pity it wasn't the *Bonhomme Richard*—they tell me that's the name of the pirate's own ship."

It was warm in the room. Firelight shone on well-polished brasses, on gleaming silver and discreetly shining mahogany. The tea was hot and fragrant, the scones light and buttery. Mrs. Scott was a famous housekeeper. She had learned that at the Honorable Mrs. Ogilvy's select school where she went to be "finished off." She had learned there also never to loll in her chair, but to sit always as she sat now, bolt upright without touching the back of the chair. An anxious and careful mother she was, too.

"Your hair's wet, Wattie, my lamb. Sit on the creepie before the fire and let it dry."

What with the fire and all the soft gleamings in the room, the warmth of tea after the long cold day, Walter was soon drowsy. With a yawn that fairly cleft him to his toes he propped himself against John and looked under heavy lids at Tom, who was staring in absorption at a cake he had just taken a bite out of. He liked Tom better than any of his brothers, but he'd rather have John like *him*. If John liked him, maybe the other lads in the Square would. Maybe they'd forget he was a lamiter. He was glad he'd asked to go to the High School.

He brought up his nodding head with a jerk.

"——just *like* Invernahyle," Mrs. Cockburn was saying, "and all the rest of the mad Highlanders. Ye might think after all the uproar they raised against the house of Hanover in the '15 and the '45, they'd have some fellow feeling for the Americans. But all ye have to do is whisper there's an enemy of Royal Geordie's about, and they're drawing their claymores before ye've finished your sentence. *Rejoice,* would he? I'll wad ye he would."

She herself had been a fervent Whig in the '45, had even been in some personal danger from the Highlanders because of an irreverent parody she had written on Prince Charlie's shabby court at Holyrood. I would have been with Charlie, if I had been living then, thought Walter. . . .

When he woke again, Mrs. Cockburn's maid had come with pattens and a lantern and Mrs. Cockburn, rising to don her cloak, was still talking sixteen to the dozen, this time about a ball she had given in her tiny house in Crichton Street.

"My house is juist the widow's cruse. Our fiddlers sat where the cupboard is, and they danced in both rooms; the table was stuffed into the window and we had plenty of room. I wish your Robert could have been here for it. Nine couples were always dancing. It made the bairns vastly happy. Anne, that puir laddie is asleep on his feet."

As they staggered up the stairs to bed, John held out something in his hand to Walter. "Here," he said.

"What is't?" said Walter, peering at the sticky mass in the darkness.

"Jube."

"Oh. *Thanks.*" He felt a glow of pleasure that fairly prickled the roots of his hair. By jing, that meant something, John's sharing his jube.

His cheek still bulged with the toffee when he tumbled into bed, rolled over against Tom, drew a long, exhausted sigh, and for the first time since he had come home, fell asleep without a longing thought of Aunt Jenny and the farm.

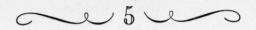
THE YARD

THE tutor was not a success. Nobody liked him, not even Mr. Scott, who had chosen him with much care and might have been the more warmly disposed toward him on that account.

After the tutor departed, the family relaxed and felt better. And one morning when smoke went up from every chimney in a thin feather, as if stiffened by the frost in the air, Walter went with John to the High School.

They arrived just as old Buie the janitor pulled the bell-rope. The school was in a hollow, with the ridge of the Canongate on one side and the bulk of Arthur's Seat behind it. Tall gray buildings made the other sides of a cup that held an incredible din, the clamor of nearly five hundred boys pouring into the Yard, and above all the shouts and scufflings, the harsh clang of the bell.

Ancient as the school itself was, the school building was new. Its tawny stone was still undimmed by smoke; it had the long straight lines and the plain roof of the new classical style. No crow-stepped gables or pointed windows here. All was square, airy, and modern.

The welter of boys became a stream, flowing through the pillared portico into the school house. The backs of heads began to show through the windows, moving restlessly, sometimes half turning or ducking down.

Walter felt very small. There were so many boys and they all seemed to be bigger than he was. They all looked alike. They wore different colored coats and waistcoats and the biggest boys had tails to their jackets, but their faces might all have been made from the same pattern. Only their eyes were different; some looked at Walter without seeing him; some gleamed with curiosity; some, a few, softened with pity. On the doorstep the press was tightest. Walter felt as if he were being pushed through a forest of hard rough elbows.

One other boy went through the door with him, a boy with a pale pointed face and quick dark eyes. "New!" the lad said and kicked him on the shin.

The room they came into was the Long Hall, a great room filled with wooden forms. Every boy knew where he belonged.

"You're to be in Mr. Fraser's class," said John. "Sit there."

Walter sat down hesitantly on the end of a bench. When another lad came along he slid toward the middle. Now he was next to a gentle-looking boy with light brown eyes and mouse-colored hair. He could not see the boy who had kicked him. He looked for John and saw him half-way across the room with his elbow on another lad's shoulder.

The masters came in. One in a gown took his place before a reading desk on the platform. Boys who had been standing up sat down with a thud, and legs that had been sprawling in the aisles disappeared under the benches. A hush fell.

"That's Dr. Adam," whispered the lad beside Walter. The Rector's face was hidden from his view by a boy's head, but his voice carried into every corner of the room, a strong, warm voice, resonant and deliberate. He was reading from the Bible.

" 'For wisdom is a defence, and money is a defence; but the excellency of knowledge is, that wisdom giveth life to them that have it.' "

They bowed their heads for the prayer. It was cold in the room, thought Walter, and stuffy.

A great clatter followed the amen like a period at the end of a sentence. The scraping of benches, the shuffling of feet on the wooden floor, the stamp of feet on stone steps. Five turnpike staircases went up from the back of the auditorium to the five classrooms above. Circular stairs are hard for lame legs. Walter clung to the outer wall where the steps were widest. Some boys passed him in a rush, some, caught behind him, breathed impatiently.

The *dux,* who kept order in the classroom till the master came, told Walter because he was new to take the lowest place. The room was filled with boys, and the last seat seemed so far from the master's desk that Walter thought you might sit there all day without being troubled by anything that was going on up in front.

Mr. Luke Fraser came in, and after a moment or two of assembling himself and his effects, said loudly:

"Is Gualterus Scott here today? If he is, he will come forward, please."

Walter, not recognizing his own name in its scholastic form, sat on in dreamy obscurity until the boy beside him nudged him; then, embarrassed, he started up and went forward to receive two books from the master's hands. He felt everybody's eyes upon him as he limped back down the room, and he was glad to take his seat again and be very busy looking at the books. One of them was Adam's *Grammar;* the other he did not see, though he turned the pages and ran his finger down the margins as though he were hunting for some special passage.

When his face cooled and he lifted his head again, the boys in the first form were translating the lesson. Walter's neighbors were engaged in various surreptitious pursuits. There was a good deal of whispering and wriggling which grew louder and less guarded until it drew the wrath of Mr. Fraser, who uttered harsh words and stamped his foot so sharply that a cloud of dust rose around him. In the burst of industry that followed, the lad next to Walter showed him the place in his book.

The Latin was much more difficult than the Latin which he had met at Mr. Leechman's school, and even the boys in the middle forms seemed to be able to cope satisfactorily with it. It occurred to Walter that he might have some trouble in rising far from the foot of the class. Oh well, he thought, they're all bigger than me;

it's no disgrace to be low in a class where you're the youngest.

Slowly Mr. Fraser came down the aisle. Over and over the lesson was droned. Some boys moved up a place or two, some went down. Three boys ahead of Walter failed on the meaning of a word that Wattie knew. Up he went three places. No longer at the very bottom he began to entertain hopes of further progress. He had no thought of reaching the heights of the first form, but he would like to rise enough to get near the fireplace in the middle of the room. It was cold here; already his hands felt stiff and numb.

The boy who had kicked him was on one side of him in his new position. Walter managed to step heavily on his foot when he took his place, and the boy grinned cheerfully. On the other side was a lad whom he had heard called Johannes Irving. They measured each other with their eyes, but neither made any advances.

It seemed hours before the bell rang and they all poured out into the yard where the air was fresh and gusty and clouds raced low in the sky overhead. James Brown in a white apron was out by the gate with his barrow of pies and jube, and boys were streaming down the wynd to the tenement where Lucky Brown, his wife, kept her shop—just like, Walter thought, the lawyers crossing Parliament Close to the coffee-house for their meridian.

He looked for John, but every way he turned he was blocked by a lad in his own class.

"Let me by."

"I don't think I will. I—don't—think—I—like—your
—face."

"What's the matter with it?"

"I don't like it. That's what's the matter with it."

"Well," said Walter reasonably, "you don't have to
look at it."

"That's just it—I do. *You* don't, but I do." Evidently
feeling that this sally was very successful, he threw back
his head and cackled shrilly. Some of the bystanders
joined in. Encouraged, he swaggered a bit. "I think I'll
have to spoil it for you." A little crowd gathered to
watch.

Walter understood. This was what they did to new
boys. He set his jaw, doubled up his fists, and waited.

The other boy suddenly turned away. "It's no use to
hargle-bargle with a cripple," he muttered.

Anger raced hotly through Walter's blood. If he just
had two good legs. If he just had Marian. He thought
of the knights of old riding at each other on horseback
with leveled lances.

"I'll fight anybody my own size," he said doggedly,
"if I can fight mounted."

Some big boys from the Rector's class had stopped
to see what was going on. "That's an idea," cried one of
them. "Mount the little tinklers and let them fight it
out."

A fight always drew a crowd. There were plenty of lads
to run behind the school house and bring out a long
deal board which they stretched like a trestle between
the step and a wooden box set on end; plenty more to

find rope with which to lash the two combatants face to face astraddle their wooden horse.

The tall lad tied the last knot and stepped back. "Fight away, fire-eaters."

The fire-eaters looked at each other a little dubiously. This would not be like the rolling over and over on the ground and punching at random of which the battles of the younger fry usually consisted. Walter was thinking that he had never been in any kind of fight before, and that the other boy was very near and looked bigger than he had thought. They raised their fists.

The first blow caught Wattie on the ear and made his head ring. The next one glanced off his guarding arm. He saw his opponent's face in a blur and went for it with his fist. His arm was longer than he knew and he felt the impact all the way to his shoulder; his knuckles came back with the print of teeth on them.

He heard shouting, and set about him with both arms at once. He got a punch on the nose and one in the left eye in quick succession. His head was bursting. He tasted blood on his lips.

"You had enough?" he heard his adversary pant.

"No!"

He drew himself up as far as he could for the cords around his waist and launched himself against his enemy. His long arms were like flails that brushed aside the other's fists as if they were stalks of grain.

"*You* had enough?"

Through the confused shouts of the onlookers and the din in his own head the lad's answer reached him but faintly, but he gathered that it was in the negative. The big boy put a hand on the shoulder of each one and held them apart.

"You've both had enough," he said. "Shake hands now."

The mists cleared away. Walter saw that the other boy's lip was cut. His own eye was swelling, and blood poured from his nose down the front of his yellow waistcoat. They shook hands gingerly. Both fists were sore. Dismounting from the board Walter leaned over to rub his leg ruefully; he had not realized till the battle was over how very hard and uncomfortable that board had been.

The tall boy patted him on the back. "Good fighter for a little tinkler," he said approvingly. Walter glowed. He thought of William Boltfoot and doubted if even he could have done much better under the circumstances.

John Irving on one side of him and a boy named Adam Ferguson on the other escorted him to the well to put cold water on his eye and nose.

"Button your waistcoat over on the other side," said Adam. "Then it won't show."

Walter fumbled for the buttons. This double-breasted arrangement was convenient. The water cooled his throbbing face.

"Eh sirs, that was a fight!" exulted Irving. "It was as good as a ballad."

Walter lifted his face out of the bucket and looked at him in surprise.

"Do you know about ballads too?"

"Do *you?*"

The bell rang and they had to go up to the classroom again. Walter was tired, so tired that he could hardly stay awake while the slow drone of questions and answers came down the forms. He missed the question that reached him at long last, and lost the places that he had gained in the morning. Irving pretended to shed tears over his going and Wattie grinned back through his weariness. After all, it wasn't the classroom that mattered; it was the Yard.

BUTTON

I T's the button that does it! The thought woke Walter out of a sound sleep as sharply as if it had rung a bell in his ear. It *was* the button. Yes, by jing. Every time Davy Douglas stood up to recite in class he twiddled with that third button on his waistcoat. He would stand twisting it thoughtfully in his fingers, and after a moment he would come forth with the right answer to Mr. Fraser's question. The button first and then the answer. If it weren't for Davy Douglas and his button, Walter would have been up by the fire by now. He had risen far in four months, but he couldn't get past Davy.

And if somebody cut off that button?

Wattie blew out a long breath and saw it turn white in the early morning grayness. It was cold and the air had a fresh, raw smell. I'll wad ye it's snowed, thought Walter. Tom was asleep still, rolled up in a knot with his knees near his chin and his rear butting into Walter. It was simple enough to climb out over him, leaving him groaning and muttering crossly and burrowing his head into the pillow.

It had snowed. A white drift lay on the window sill

where it had sifted in, though the window was of course closed tight; the square panes of glass were made round at the bottom by the snow that clung to the outside of them. In the Meadows the black boles of the trees were streaked with white and all the ground was covered so that only a trail of footsteps showed where the path lay hidden. Skyward to the right on the Castle Rock the little crannies where owl and weasel nested in summer held the snow as if they had been cups, but the precipice and the sides of the buildings above were bare. Highest of all the roof of the barracks was overlaid with snow that seemed to merge with the sky where more snow, layers and layers of it, hung ready to fall.

The door banged open and John clattered into the room. He was already dressed to go out, his muffler wound three times around his throat and tied at the back.

"Snow! They'll be manning the Cowgate Port. Ye've no time to waste dawdling."

He scooped up a clammy handful from the window-sill, passed it swiftly over Walter's surprised face, and was off with shrill whoop that seemed to hang in the air even after his boots were heard stamping on the lowest stair step.

Unperturbed, Walter dried his face on a towel so stiff and cold that it hurt his skin, and decided that that was sufficient wash for a cold morning, especially since the water in the pitcher had a crust of ice across the top of it. He stuffed his shirt-tail into his brown corduroy breeches, tied the black ribbon at his throat, and fast-

ened on his red waistcoat with fingers so stiff with cold
that he had to blow on them to thaw them out. The buttons reminded him of Davy Douglas. Yes, by jing!

Sweeping the covers off Tom, he swung himself down
the stairs with one hand on the banister and the other
braced against the wall in the one-legged hop he had
perfected for speed, whistling as he went a popular song
that proclaimed:

> The old man's mare's dead,
> The puir man's mare's dead,
> The old man's mare's dead,
> A mile aboon Dundee.

A crowd was seething around the Cowgate Port when
he and John got there half an hour before school time.
Snowballs and yells filled the air. Already the bigger
boys had swarmed to the top of the massive old city gate
and from there were pelting passersby with snowballs.
The Toon Rottens, as the Town Guard were nicknamed,
were rushing about, brandishing their Lochaber axes,
shouting and stuttering with rage at the Hie Schule
laddies who made them this trouble every year when
snow came. The old Highlanders were at a disadvantage.
The bad lads perched high in the air, safely out of reach,
would knock off their tape-bound cocked hats with snowballs and then pelt their red coats when they stooped
to pick up their headgear. The small fry were in every
wynd and close manufacturing more snowballs with
which they ran to supply the fighters above. They were
about as active and annoying and hard to catch as

fleas, but now and then one of them was nabbed and was well shaken and cuffed before he either managed to wriggle away or was taken to the guard house in the High Street, there to remain as an example until his father, in what state of mind may be imagined, came to claim him.

Walter was slow enough to be in considerable danger of getting caught. Deciding that it would be safer as well as more interesting to be on top of the Cowgate Port, he began a determined effort to get there, John Irving and Adam Ferguson boosting him from below. It was a matter of getting a toe-hold in the unevenness of the stone, of embracing a square, rough pillar with arms and knees. He was soon puffing and panting and he could feel Irving grunting beneath him.

"That's it, Wattie. I've got your leg. Put your other foot on that wee ledge there——"

He was making progress.

Then Davy Douglas began coming down.

"The bell's going to ring in a minute," he said. "I saw Buie go out."

"What if it does?" retorted Wattie, feeling his fingers slip while Davy practically sat on his head. "Everybody else will be late too. I'm going up."

But there was no getting up past Davy coming down. They fell together in a heap on the trampled snow and mud, Wattie's head against Davy's ribs. He saw the third waistcoat button, looser than the rest, dangling within a few inches of his eyes, and almost without thinking he closed his fingers round it and snapped it off in one sharp tug.

Davy got up and brushed off his knees. "There's the bell! I told you!"

He made off at top speed with heels and elbows at all angles. He had not noticed that his button was gone.

For the present the fray was over. The Toon Rottens stood back and watched while the schoolboys streamed up the wynd to the Yard. There were a final Gaelic imprecation or two, a few scattered snowballs, before the school doors swallowed up the last stragglers.

During prayers Wattie's fingers were busy in his pocket with the penny he had for jube and Davy Douglas's button. It was a brass button with a shank, and it had the slightly greasy surface that brass acquires. He was vastly amused to think that Davy hadn't felt him yank that button off. He wanted to tell Irving about it, but decided that it would be more fun to wait and see what happened in class.

"Watch Davy," he whispered on the way up the turnpike stairs.

His place was just below the middle of the room now, with Adam Ferguson on his left, and Davy at the top of the form. He could not forbear whispering to Adam as they sat down, "Watch Davy."

Adam watched obediently for some time before he reported, "He's got a streak of mud on his cheek."

Mr. Luke Fraser's progress down the aisle seemed slower than ever this morning. Wattie, though he hadn't finished his own work, gave those around him help and advice as generous as it was inaccurate until the master was within two or three forms of him, when he settled down to listen attentively. Nothing could distract him now, no nudgings or whisperings or sly allusions.

"Davidius Douglas, you will repeat the third rule for the use of the subjunctive."

Walter looked over his shoulder and caught Irving's eye. "Watch him now," he mouthed silently. They both leaned forward a little.

Davy stood up confidently. His hand fumbled for his third button, and found nothing. He looked confused.

"Please, sir, the subjunctive is used——" He stammered. A wave of red seeped up from his neck and washed over his face. He looked bewildered, as if he did not know what had happened to him. "The subjunctive is used——" His fingers fluttered a little, aimlessly. He hesitated and sat down, suddenly, blankly, like a collapsed bladder.

Three boys came in between who apparently had never heard of the subjunctive. Walter jumped up and rattled off the rule glibly. Davy's face, as he changed places with him, was mild and puzzled. Why, he didn't know, Wattie realized in a flash, that his button was gone. He didn't even know that he twirled his button. Wattie suddenly felt mean.

He swallowed—and swallowed the wrong way. He began to cough. He sat at the top of the form and coughed and choked till his throat felt raw, his face burned and his eyes bulged. Everybody around him was more than zealous about thumping him on the back; somebody suggested holding him up by the heels and shaking him. Any diversion was welcome, and they made the most of this one.

Mr. Fraser, at first impatient, then angry, then concerned, told him to go down to the well and get a drink of water.

The icy water quickly stopped the tickle in his throat, but he coughed a few more times for Buie's benefit, and slowly drank another dipperful while he considered the possibilities of this quite unlooked-for bit of good fortune. From where he stood he could see the clock on the steeple of the Tron church, and it was almost half-past eleven. No reasonable person would expect him to go back to the classroom for just a few minutes. If he went to Lucky Brown's now, he could buy his jube and get a place in the ingle-neuk before the bell rang. After the big boys got into the shop the little fellows hadn't a chance.

The snow underfoot in the Yard and in the wynd was dirty and wet and nasty, but on the roofs of the high buildings it was still clean, and on the slopes of Arthur's Seat it lay untouched. Salisbury Crags were red and forbidding against its whiteness, and the wind that blew over it was raw and fresh in the nostrils. In Lucky Brown's shop the air was warm from the fire and heavy with spices and with the fragrance of baking tarts. After the thin cold outside air, this felt so thick and warm that you could almost eat it.

Lucky herself, with sparse locks of hair escaping from

under her round-eared cap, was bustling back and forth between the oven and James's barrow. She gave a little squawk when she saw Walter. "Whisht, is't that late?"

"I'm early. I want a pennyworth of jube."

"Tak' it yoursel'. I've no time to wait on you. *I* make the jube and *I* make the tarts and the buns—would ye no think he could pack up his ain barra? But no, he'll no fash his beard about onything. I've got sax things tae do wi' each hand—pick yoursel' a lump o' jube that looks like a pennyworth. Na, na, no that ane. The yin next it."

"What you need," said Wattie, taking his jube to the basket of essences to doctor it according to his fancy, "is a brownie to do your odd jobs for you." He took the stopper from the bottle of oil of cloves and touched it to his jube.

"A brownie! Humph. A James Brownie. I'd be settisfied if *he* wae do a hand's turn ance and again."

With his head tilted judiciously on one side Wattie added the least suspicion of cinnamon, and then rolled the whole lump in the pot of ground ginger. He tasted it. By jing, that was just right. He'd never had time to fix it exactly the way he wanted it before, with the crowd of big boys jostling him out of the way.

Luxuriously he settled himself in the ingle-neuk. This was *good*. Warm and spicy and shut in. A picture of the classroom flashed across his mind, with Davy Douglas feeling for his button and looking confused. He went hot all over and felt mean. Pshaw.

"Brownies come at night," he said loudly, "and do all kinds o' jobs for you. And you don't have to pay them anything. If you put out a bowl of milk or a piece of cheese for them it insults them and they go away. I mind one story Tibbie Hunter used to tell about a lady that made a wee green coat for her brownie—she felt so grateful to him—and left it out where he'd be sure to find it. He took it, but it hurt his feelings so much that she'd think of paying him, that he never came again."

"Perhaps he thocht she might wish to tak' the coat back," suggested Lucky Brown, insensitive to the finer feelings of the brownie. "Losh preserve us, here comes the callants."

They were all over the shop, squabbling and pushing around the basket of essences, devouring pies, pestering Lucky for more jube, more buns, more tarts.

"There's apple there. Six apple tarts under yer very neb."

"But we want plum. Lucky, we want plum. Lucky Brown, we—want—plum."

"Havers, do ye want to deave me? Plum indeed. And if it was plum there ye'd want apple. Here, tak' yer plum."

Wattie managed to save places for his own particular friends, Irving and Adam and Lordie Ramsay. They were squeezed into the corner so tight that they almost ate each other's jube, but uncomfortable though they were, it was a triumph just to be there, the only small boys in all that noisy crowd about the fire.

"The sound of jube being chewed was heard in the land," said Wattie airily.

Adam opened his mouth wide and gave three extra loud chews for answer. He was very much elated over being there, and his blue eyes under their pointed brows were bright and eager.

"Wattie, go on with the story you started yesterday."

"Where was I?" Well he knew where he had stopped, but it made a more dramatic beginning if your listeners gave you a shove.

"He was goin' through the wood o' Pitmurkie."

"Oh yes. Well, it was pitch dark, and the horse turned this way and that through the trees till they came to the thickest and darkest part of the whole wood, and there was a castle, with gates and a courtyard and portcullis – all dark. From inside came the sound of pipes and fiddles and hallooing and shouting and all kinds of skulduddery——"

It was warm in the ingle-neuk and dim with the red firelight and noisy with the crowd milling around them. They all put their heads close so as to hear him.

"He won through to the oak parlor, and there they were, all birling red wine and their faces white as—as snow. Gray-white like——"

He broke off. Davy Douglas had wormed his way to them through the crowd, smiling and still unconscious that any wrong had been done him. That unconsciousness of his was too much for Wattie. He held out what was left of his jube.

"Here," he said, "you can have it. Major Weir the

wizard was there," he went on hastily, pretending not to see the surprise and indignation rising in Adam's face, "and Claverhouse that persecuted the Covenanters, and a hantle of others—and they were all *dead*."

7

BROUGHTON'S SAUCER

WALTER was sick. He lay in bed in his mother's dressing-room with a Lochaber ax, an ancient claymore, and a rusty Highland hunting knife among the bedclothes with him, and a scuffed leather volume on the table beside him, along with Anne's baby, which she felt sure would comfort him, and a glass that had contained a nauseous draught. The house was quiet. The March afternoon was closing in early, and it was too dark to read any longer. He'd read all the best parts of *Richard III* anyhow. It was bad luck to have to stay in bed on Saturday when there was all the rest of the week to choose from.

He yawned prodigiously. This time last year he was at Sandyknowe with Aunt Janet and Grandmother Scott and Uncle Tom. A day like this, when the wind howled outside, they used to sit in that clean, clean parlor, Grandmother with her spinning-wheel by the fire, Aunt Janet with her book, Wattie stretched out on the hearth-rug, and Uncle Tom playing "Sour Plums in Galashiels" on the pipes. Last year he had Marian to ride. He thought about her so hard that he could see her, her nose soft as velvet in his hand, her brown eyes, slightly bulging, her funny stiff eyelashes, her long mane and tail that looked so fluffy and felt so harsh. She was so little she could go anywhere, along the narrowest ledges and up the steepest places around Smailholm Tower, and he had even ridden her into the farmhouse. Not that she got to stay long. But there hadn't been the fuss about it that there would have been here.

How long ago that seemed. Years and years and years, like a dream, or like something that happened to somebody else. He looked back on himself as if he were a quite separate being to whom he felt somewhat superior. How terribly young that other Walter Scott was, how ignorant, how bumptious. He blushed for him, remembering—but that was farther back than last year, of course—how he had shouted out the verses of Hardyknute when the minister came to call, and how the minister had stood it as long as he could and then had stamped away saying, "As well try to talk into the mouth of a cannon as where that child is!"

There would be lambs on the farm now, all the little new lambs with their brittle legs and their lively tails and their silly baby faces. He could remember way back into the mists, when he was really little, being wrapped in a warm sheepskin, a new sheepskin just taken from the sheep, and put down on the farmhouse floor. His grandfather dangled something before him, a watch perhaps, and he struggled to crawl towards it. They thought it would help his lame leg. Aunt Jenny had told him about it so often that he did not know how much he really remembered, and how much he got from her stories; he wasn't sure, for instance, of the sheepskin, but he knew he remembered the firelight and the gleaming thing, and Grandfather's face with the blue eyes and the white hair waving around it. It had looked so big to him, he must have been very small himself. Grandfather was no longer at Sandyknowe. He could remember sealing the funeral letters with black wax.

The bed was hot and wrinkled and full of crumbs. He sat up and thrashed around a bit with his arms and yawned again. He felt all right now, really, though not one bit hungry, but he rather thought it would be just as well not to recover too quickly. There was no sense in missing all the Saturday holiday, and then getting up in time for two sermons and the catechism Sunday.

He hunted among the bedclothes for the Lochaber ax, lifted it in his hands and looked at it. Invernahyle had brought it at last, and a claymore too, as well as the whinger he had promised. Lochaber axes weren't used for much any more, though the Toon Rottens still carried them. They belonged to the days when men used to besiege castles with hand-to-hand fighting. There was a hook on the end of the ax. You hooked it over a bit of masonry or the top of a wall above your head and swung yourself up by it. Then when you were up on the top you swung your ax and whacked off your enemy's head, or cleft his battle helmet through to his shoulders.

Walter lifted the ax as high as his arms would reach. It swayed heavily in his hands. Holding it by the **very** end he could just manage to reach up and slip the hook over the rod that held green damask draperies at the top of the window. That's the way it went. Then you pulled yourself up, hand over hand——

"Walter Scott, are you daft? To be playing with such a thing in bed! You'll have the curtains down about our ears in a minute, and it's a miracle that ax-head didna go through the window pane."

Scolding and sputtering, his mother went for the dangling battle-ax, but was too short to reach it. Walter stood up on the bed and took it down for her.

"It's easy to see Invernahyle has no children—he'd never have given you these instruments. Lochaber axes and claymores are no play-toys, no, nor whingers either. Rusty and dull as this one is, it could give a body a sair dunt on the head."

Her skirts switching with decision, she took them from him and stood them up in a corner of the room.

"I'm saving them for a museum, Mother."

"You could have better objects in a museum than dangerous things like these, commemorating blood and death."

"I don't think of blood and death. I think of scaling castle walls and waving your claymore over your head and not being afraid of any man that walks——"

"Aye. Courage. Courage is very fine, but there's all kinds of courage, though most people don't recognize any but the noisiest and showiest kind——"

"Mother, you got anything else I could put in my museum?"

"Here, wrap this coat round you and sit in the chair

while I put your bed to rights. Let me feel you—and stick out your tongue."

Her hand on his forehead was light and cool and firm. He touched his chin with his tongue.

"You've no trace of fever; you'll be able to go to church tomorrow if the weather holds."

"Mother, you got anything else I could put in my museum?"

"I think I may have. I'll look in the cupboard when I get this bed straight. Mercy on us, you'll have been churning about!"

He climbed back into the smooth fresh bed and watched her search in the cupboard, standing on a footstool and holding the candle high with one hand while with the other she shifted little rolls of paper and boxes of odds and ends and silver and china objects without handles or spouts that had been saved for the mending. The candlelight shone on the white ruffles of her cap, on her kerchief, and picked up the sheen of her shot-silk dress.

"Here's something—it's not what I was hunting for—but you can have it."

It was a colored print, a little faded and limp, of Bonnie Prince Charlie, with his plaid over his shoulder and his bonnet on the side of his head. He was young and handsome and yellow-haired.

"Oh, I like that fine. I wish I had lived in the days of the '45. I would have gone out for Charlie."

"And you the son of a good Whig. Your father would

have had something to say about that. Here's what I was looking for. It's the saucer that went with the teacup Murray of Broughton drank out of."

Walter took the saucer in his hand and turned it over, a little disappointed.

"Where's the cup?"

"Gone wherever little broken bits of china go. It was shattered to bits on the paving-stones in the College Wynd."

"What for? When?"

"It was when I was a deal younger and sillier and more curious than I am now. We were living in the College Wynd, and every night a stranger all muffled up in a black cloak would come in a sedan chair to the door. Your father would receive him in his study, and for half an hour I would hear low voices on the far side of a closed door, and then the stranger would come out wound up in his cloak, get into his chair and go away again. Night after night it happened, and never a word did your father say to me about it."

"Did he always come at the same time?"

"Exactly the same time. I'd watch him come out of the window and I'd watch him go, peering over the stair rail, and at length I was so eaten up with curiosity I could endure it no longer. So one night when the two of them, your father and that other, had been closeted together almost the length of their usual time, I took a tea-tray and I went and knocked on the door and invited the gentlemen to drink a dish of tea with me."

"What happened?" Walter could picture the stocky little lady with her straight back and the tray in her hand, the gleam in her eye.

"The strange gentleman rose and thanked me courteously, and drank off the steaming tea as if it had been wine, and cold. Your father's face was set; he waved aside the cup I offered him, and after one look at him I never thought of tasting the third cup that I'd brought for myself. The stranger bowed good-by; he threw his cloak around his shoulder and went out. We heard the footsteps of his chairmen growing fainter as they went up the wynd."

"Then what happened?"

"Your father went to the window and opened it, and he flung out the teacup the stranger had drunk from. I'll never forget the little noise it made shivering to pieces on the stones below. And he said, 'I can forgive your little curiosity, Madam, but you must pay the penalty. Neither lip of me nor of mine comes after Mr. Murray of Broughton.' "

"Was he really Murray of Broughton, who betrayed Prince Charlie?"

"Yes, he was. He had come to your father on business, and as a lawyer he couldn't refuse to see him."

"But Father's not a Jacobite anyhow, he's a Whig."

"Your father's not a Jacobite, but he has no use for a traitor, whichever side he be on."

"What did he look like, Murray of Broughton?"

"I was too excited to get a very good look at him that

night, but he was getting on in years, well-dressed and very polite in his manners."

"And this is really the very same saucer?"

"The very same. I saved it. Not that I needed it to remind me not to go meddling again in affairs that didn't concern me—I'd learned that lesson once for all—but I hadn't known before that your father could be so romantic. We had a whole set of that china, with those gold bands on the edge and the red vines. That was the first cup to go—we hadn't been married so very long When one cup gets broken the others seem to follow fast. There weren't any more thrown out of windows though."

"Mother, what happened to Murray of Broughton?"

"He died two or three years ago in a madhouse. I suppose what he had done preyed on his mind till it broke, poor man."

Walter traced with his finger the depression in the saucer where the cup had stood. It would be fine in the museum. Murray of Broughton, right in his own house, the house where he'd been born! And think of Father!

The front door banged and there was clattering on the stairs. John and Thomas and Wullie Edmonstone burst in, followed by Anne.

"Mother, can Wattie get up? We're going to give a play and we need him."

"Wullie's uncle took him to see *Douglas* at the Theatre Royal, and now we're going to give a play."

Douglas was no good. It took too many people. Wattie

knew a better play than that. He bounced up and down in bed.

"I know a better play than *Douglas*. Let's give *Richard III*." If he got up and took part in a play tonight, he'd have to go to church tomorrow sure—both services, with the catechism and Blair's *Sermons* for light reading-matter between times. Oh well. . . . "*Richard III* is the play for ye. And I'll be Duke of Gloucester—the limp will do for the hump. And Mother, could we no get Mrs. Cockburn to come in for audience?"

He wanted to show her Broughton's saucer. She was a Whig, and she made fun of Charlie and his short-lived court at Holyroodhouse—he'd like her to know how that other staunch Whig, his father, had tossed a gold-banded china cup out of the window because a traitor had drunk out of it.

8

THE GUTTED HADDIE

THEY'RE coming."

"Quick! Hide."

Walter and John Irving dived into the nearest doorway just in time. Outside in the narrow street a gang of High School lads, headed by John Scott and Wullie Edmonstone, went cruising along evidently in search of something with which to fill their Saturday morning. The black pocket in which the two lads were hiding was the common stairway for the half-dozen families who lived in this old "land"; it was dark and chilly after the bright summer day outside and it smelled of old stone, old dust, old lives.

"They'll be gone now. I'm going to look out."

"No, wait. Someone's coming."

They heard a sturdy tread coming down the twisting stone steps above them, smelled the clean, sharp odor of fresh fish, felt someone pass close to them, her many stiff canvas petticoats pressed against them in the narrow, dark entry. They knew even before she stepped out into the light that it was a Musselburgh fishwife with her creel on her back. She paused a moment in the doorway, adjusting the band of webbing that went over her fore-head and held her basket of fish in place between her shoulders.

"Take a look up and down the wynd for us, hinny," said Walter, "and see are the callants all gone by."

She gave a squawk of surprise and leaned over to peer at them in the shadow.

"Lawks, I didna see ye there. Twa bonnie laddies."

Good-naturedly she went out into the street and looked up and down.

"Na, there's naebody in sicht, forbye a wee lassie re-turning frae the flesher's wi' a soup bone, and an auld mon sitting on his doorstane in the sunshine. Ye're no frichtit o' them?" she added teasingly.

"My good woman," said John grandly, "we're no frichtit o' a'body."

"It's a dangerous plot," said Walter in a sepulchral tone. Dangerous enough for him and Irving at that, if they got caught. They'd never live it down. To go off on a Saturday holiday with a parcel of books to read! He could imagine the scorn of John and the jeers of Wullie Edmonstone and worst of all the disgust of Walter's own band of followers who did honor to him for his prowess in the yard. "Come away, Irving. The coast is clear."

Sunshine lay lightly over street and houses, bringing to life the colors hidden in the gray stone, so that it looked no longer merely gray, but rose-colored too, and tawny, and dimly purple in the shadows. Over the way in the long back garden of a house in the Canongate it glinted on the thick leaves of a tree and made splashes of light on the grass beneath. It was August, and the birds were silent, all but a robin redbreast that hopped on the stone wall and sang his piece twice over before he flew away. Walter hooked his arm through Irving's and they started off down the street toward Holyroodhouse.

"Losh presairve us," said the young fishwife behind them. "A dangerous plot, he says, and him a wee lamiter!"

Wattie turned. "I'm no that lame. I'm off to climb Arthur's Seat."

"Havers," she said admiringly.

"By the Gutted Haddie," he added.

"Havers."

Irving carried the books and Wattie the packet of bread and cheese. They stopped at the corner of the street and looked both ways before they crossed. From somewhere behind them came the sound of shouts and the thwacking of sticks and pounding of feet. John and Wullie and their men had started something. They skirted around Holyroodhouse without meeting anybody and started up the narrow trail that led over the top of Salisbury Crags. They could have reached the nook in the rocks that they were heading for more easily by going round through the town and entering the King's Park near St. Leonard's, but they preferred this. They had been spending their Wednesday and Saturday holidays this way all summer and they knew just how to get the most fun out of it.

"Go on with Sir Nigel," said John.

"No, you go on with Sir Amadace," said Walter politely, and without waiting for Irving to draw his breath began hastily,

"Sir Nigel had lost his way completely in the desert. His horse was gone, and the sun was burning him up in his armor, and he was in despair. Suddenly he saw these huge birds called Urgs flying about and he got an idea. He caught one in a net and tamed it and taught it to carry him. Then he climbed on it and flew away, guiding it with his belt, like a bit. When they got over the Mediterranean suddenly it wobbled—it must have been tired or something—and kersplash! they both fell into the sea. There's something like that in the book I was telling you about that I got out of the library."

"The *school library?* There's nothing good in that. The best thing they have is Plutarch."

"No, this is good. *Voyages and Travels* it's called."

"Sir Amadace," said Irving firmly, "was fighting the Saracens. He had drunk a toast out of a death's-head, and he . . ."

Walter was willing enough to let Sir Amadace have his way for the present. They had reached a steep bit and the wind was blowing, a fresh warm wind that came up from the Firth and swept over the whin bushes on Whinny Hill, and pushed and tugged at you till it made walking hard. They were now on the very crest of the ridge called Salisbury Crags. On one side of them was the Hunter's Bog, the mysterious low land lying in a

cup between Salisbury Crags and Arthur's Seat. On the
other side the crags dropped off sheerly almost beneath their feet, and down there below them lay Edinburgh, hazy in the smoke of its chimneys, with its
church steeples, the Tron and the Shrewsbury and the
crown of St. Giles, lifted above the welter of roofs, and
the Castle riding over all like a ship, small in the distance, but proud.

"Anybody looking up from down there would see us
against the sky like two toy men," said Walter, pausing
to rest his leg. He felt the sky all around him, and the
wind, and the sudden dimming of the sunlight as a
cloud sailed overhead. He watched its shadow move
slowly over the Hunter's Bog.

"Well, Sir Nigel thrashed around in the water. The
bird sank, but Sir Nigel kept afloat, swimming on his
back," resumed Walter. It was easier walking now, and
there was room for them to go abreast.

By all the laws of nature, Sir Nigel and Sir Amadace
should have come to glorious but painful ends Saturdays
ago, so terrible and so frequent were the dangers they
were exposed to, but neither Walter nor Irving could
bear to part with them and so the heroes were always
rescued miraculously in the nick of time.

"Here's where we go down."

They had discovered it one Wednesday afternoon in
June, a place in the rocks that was like a little room. It
was floored with fine soft grass and harebells; high rocks
rose behind it and lower ones hid it from view in front.

Sitting there in the sunshine you could look out between the rocks over green and secret distances to the
Lammermuirs, but nobody could see you.

It was something of a feat to get to it. The first time
they had done it, Irving had to go down first and Walter
had climbed down onto his shoulder, grazing his hand
and tearing the knee of his stocking as he went. Now
that he had had practice, however, he could manage
very well, with a foot in a cranny here and a quick
grip of a jagged place there, and a final push and a drop
on all fours onto the grass.

He was up again at once, dusting his hands and knees
and looking to see if the tin box they had hidden in a
little hollow in the rocks had been tampered with. It
was rusted by the August rains, but its contents were
undisturbed. They always left a piece of paper on the
top folded in a special way so that they could tell by a
glance if anybody had been at it.

There was a notebook in the box, in which they kept
a record of the days they came up here and the books
they read; there was a package of Edinburgh rock
candy; an old red woolen cap that Irving put on to read
in—he could lean his head back against the rock more
comfortably—and a paper containing the beginning of
an epic poem that Walter was going to write about
the Bruce. So far he hadn't got beyond the introduc-
tion.

They sat down with their backs to the rock and their
faces toward the hills, Irving put on his cap, and they
opened the book of *Voyages and Travels*. Walter read

faster than Irving, and at the end of each two pages he
would have to wait before turning the leaf. Sometimes
he watched John's face while he was waiting, watched
the dark gray eyes traveling back and forth, back and
forth, as if jerked by a wire inside his head. He had
straight short eyelashes and a straight short nose; his
skin was very smooth and fair and there was a mole on
his right cheek. Sometimes Walter played with the
harebells in the crannies of the rock. Such slender stems,
such blue transparent petals, bending and nodding in
the breeze as if the next breath must shatter them, and
yet never being shattered. Or he looked up and saw
swallows and house martins wheeling and swooping in
the sky, making a little cheeping noise as they flew. Or
he looked out over the Lammermuirs and thought of
the heather there, the acres and acres of purple carpet-
ing those lonely stretches, and the cloud shadows shifting over them.

"Turn," said John, and he quickly read the last word
again and flipped over the page.

This was a good book. You had to skip every now
and then when the old boy got to prosing about trade
and mines and things, but you came on nuggets of ad-
venture that were pure gold. Like that one about the
man who went to see the King of the Muscovites. Sir
Nigel could do that.

John yawned. "Let's eat," he said.

They cut the hunks of bread and cheese with their
pocket knives, and walked about to stretch their legs
while they ate.

"You know," said Walter with his cheek bulging. "I really meant it about the Gutted Haddie."

He leaned over a rock and waved his piece of bread toward Arthur's Seat. From here, where it was so much nearer, it looked even higher and more frowning than it did from Edinburgh.

"I know you can climb it by the path up from Dunsappie Loch because I've seen you do it, but the Gutted Haddie is gey steep. Do ye think ye could?"

It was called the Gutted Haddie because it looked like a haddock that has been laid open with a slash of a knife—a steep gash in the rocks going straight up.

"Aiblins I could and aiblins I couldna," said Walter, quoting Tibby Hunter, "but I'd like fine to have a try."

He had fought in the school yard, he had been in many a bicker, he had climbed to the top of the Cowgate Port. They had almost forgot, those other lads, that he was a lamiter. Now he wanted to climb the Gutted Haddie, not to show them, but just for his own sake.

"Come on, then," said Irving. "Wait. Gie's some rock first."

They stowed away the box again, and Irving crammed the books into his pockets. Down they went, along the southern edge of the Hunter's Bog.

"Muschat's Cairn's down in there, where Nicol Muschat murdered his wife," said Irving. It had happened some sixty years ago, but the cairn of stones that marked the dreadful spot was still an object of awe to the Edinburgh boys.

"Man, wouldn't that be a place to meet somebody at

night, if ye were plotting something. Nobody would follow ye there."

Perhaps Sir Nigel—it had possibilities. He tried to imagine the Hunter's Bog in the moonlight: the deep shadows there would be, and the glimmer of the moon on the gray rocks, and the white face of somebody waiting beside the cairn, and now and then a cloud over the moon and everything black.

"Mother says there's legends about the witches meeting there," said Irving.

"Do ye think she knows a ballad about it?"

"I don't know. She might."

"We'll ask her." Mrs. Irving knew more ballads than anybody except maybe Aunt Janet, and Walter knew all hers by heart now. Mrs. Irving knew some he'd never even heard of, and in the late afternoons at tea time she would sometimes tell them to him. He thought some day he would write them all down just as she told them. They ought to be in a book.

The path was rising steeply now. Up, straight up they seemed to go, so straight that the green slope close-cropped by sheep fairly stared them in the face. There was nothing to hold on to, no rocks yet, and no whin bushes. Walter looked over his shoulder once and saw that the world fell away below them. They were like flies on a wall. John, ahead of him, took to going on all fours and Wattie followed his example.

"Do ye want to go back?" said Irving, pausing and looking down under his elbow.

"No."

The rocks were beginning now, and high up above them on a narrow ledge a sheep looked down at them and said "baa-aaa" in a thin, flat bleat. They had to go even more slowly and carefully now. There was no path, only some places in the rocks that were easier than others. Irving went first and tested each one out, and then stretched a hand back to Walter. They did not look down any longer, nor up either, but just took each step cautiously as it came. There was a bad place where they crossed over the top of the gash, a place where they had to ease around a bulging rock with their arms spread out over it and nothing really to hold on to.

"Just a wee bit more now," said Irving. "You'd better go ahead here and I'll boost you."

He made that one, with Irving pushing him from behind. He stood now on a little shelf, and his hands could just reach over the top of the wall of rock before him.

"I doubt ye'll have to give me another boost," he said, a little breathless.

"All right. Put yer leg up there—jump now a wee bit."

He gave a bounce and Irving boosted, grunting. His hands slipped, his knee scraped along the rock, he fell back, and for an instant it felt as if he and Irving both were going to tumble off the shelf.

"Wait. I'll go up and see can I pull you."

It was hard going, even for Irving. He scrambled and kicked wildly with his two good legs, and somehow got himself up.

"Now. Gie's yer hand."

Both their hands were damp; they squeezed painfully and slipped when the pull came. They dried them on their corduroy breeches and tried again. Walter pulled Irving down instead of Irving pulling him up.

"It's no use. We can't do it this way——"

"Can ye go back?"

"I don't want to, when I'm so near the top."

"Ye may have to."

Walter looked down and hastily turned his head away. It made him dizzy just to look. There was the gash, with a few whin bushes so deep in it that you wouldn't touch them if you started to fall. You would hurtle through the air part of the way, and then you would bound and roll without anything stopping you until you landed deep in the Hunter's Bog if you bounded to the right, or, if you went to the left, still farther away down on the roof of what looked from here like a toy cottage.

"I'll have to go up!"

He tried again, and again slipped back. He could almost do it, and then that numb leg of his would let him down.

Irving's face above him was white. "Do ye think ye could stay there without falling till I run get a ladder?"

"No, I'll try another way. Look—over here." It was longer to climb, but there were deeper footholds.

"I can't reach my hand to ye there."

"Take off your coat and reach that down to me."

Irving climbed higher and took off his coat; he dug his heels into the ground and braced himself. Walter took hold of the end of the coat let down to him. Slowly, gripping the coat with one hand and rough places in the rock with the other, one foot here, one foot there, he inched up. A plant grew in a niche above him. He made a great effort and reached for it. It held. Irving had his shoulder now. One last heave—and he was up!

"Man!" said Irving. "Man, that was a climb! I thought ye'd never make it."

He couldn't stop talking, he was so relieved. Breathing hard, Walter sat down on the edge of the rock. All spread out below him was Edinburgh, with the castle so tiny it looked as if you could hold it in your hand, and the Firth of Forth winding between green banks, and the Ochil Hills blue in the distance. He sat there, looking out over it all, and gently thumping his leg with his fist. I've beaten you, he was saying to himself, I've beaten you again!

Aloud, he said, "It looks like a dragon down there, the Firth, doesn't it?"

For the first time he realized that his hand was burning and stinging. He opened it up and saw little white spots rising on his reddened palm.

"By jing," he said, "that was a nettle I had hold of!"

THE SABBATH

S TAND up now, all of you, and let me see are you fit to
go to church."

"Oh, Mother," protested John, who, being in college
now, was easily humiliated.

Walter presented himself promptly. He was wearing
his new green coat with the tails, got for him in anticipa-
tion of his going into Dr. Adam's class after the vacation,
and he was well pleased with himself. Small use he had
for new clothes as a rule, but a coat with tails was different.

He stretched out a pair of large, long-fingered paws,
very clean, even to the wrists which were partly hidden
by the ruffles on his Sunday shirt. His old red waistcoat
and his corduroy breeches were well brushed, his Sunday shoes, a little bit short now because Sunday shoes
tend to be outgrown before they are outworn, neatly
blacked.

"Very good," said his mother, with some surprise in
her tone, and went on to Tom, who also passed muster,
though less brilliantly.

Anne was fresh and sweet as a daisy as always, and lazy

Daniel, who would do nothing for himself that he could persuade others to do for him, had been got together somehow by the cook, who adored him.

"Have you all your Bibles? Well, I think we may as well start now. Step into your father's office, Wattie, and tell him we are all ready."

Mr. Scott came at once, followed by Mr. Mitchell, the new tutor, with whom he had been discussing subjects suitable to the day.

"Where is Robert?"

"He said for us to go on ahead and he would be following in a bit." A little smile flickered at the corner of Mrs. Scott's mouth. It was gone in an instant but Walter had seen and understood it. He grinned. Robert, home on furlough from his ship, considered it "ungenteel" to go marching through the streets to church in a family party.

Mr. Scott frowned. "He will be late. He had better come now. Thomas, go tell your brother——"

"Whisht, let the lad do it his own way. He will be there in time—we are a bit early."

She had arranged that purposely, Walter surmised, got them all ready early so that Robert could save his gentility without losing his respectability. Well, Robert was a hero. He had been in Rodney's great naval engagement in April and this was his first visit home since the battle. He had earned his privileges—but just let the rest of them try anything irregular in the manner of churchgoing!

They started forth in the summer rain. Mr. and Mrs.

Scott went first under the big umbrella, followed by John and Anne; then came Mr. Mitchell with Daniel, then Walter and Tom, and finally the servants, James and Hannah and Jessie, wearing the long faces they considered appropriate to the Sabbath. The streets were silent and empty with the Sunday pall lying over them like a garment. The procession of Scotts got half-way up the Meadow Walk without seeing anybody. Anybody, that is, but Green-Breeks, and only Walter and Tom saw him. He jumped out from behind a tree and went through the motions of throwing imaginary stones at them.

Walter doubled up his fist and allowed himself the satisfaction of shaking it once before he said with propriety,

"Don't pay any attention to him, Tom. It's the Sabbath. We'll get him tomorrow."

The days were long now. It stayed light enough for a bicker every evening, and the bickers were more exciting now that Green-Breeks had come to live in the Potterrow. More dangerous, too. Green-Breeks could throw stones to a hair's breadth, and he was always among the first to advance and the last to retreat.

"Yah, yah!" he hooted after their sedate, churchgoing backs.

Walter colored. If it wasn't Sunday—— He limped doggedly on without turning his head again, although Tom reported, "The chiel's thrusting his tongue out at us now."

Nobody knew what his name was or where he came

from, except that it must have been from somewhere in the North, because he had the Gaelic. He lived with an old crone in one of the attics of a dingy house in the Potterrow, and he had quickly made himself the leader of the ancient enemies of George Square. They called him Green-Breeks because the most conspicuous article of his costume—he wore neither coat nor shoes and his shirt was sleeveless—was a large pair of green breeches which had evidently once been part of an elegant footman's livery. He was tall and fair-haired; he had clear, bright, blue eyes and a long nose that turned up at the tip.

Suddenly the church bells rang out, all at once, with every imaginable kind of jangle and note, from the Canongate Church, and from St. Paul's in York Place, from the Tron and St. Giles and Greyfriars, and even, but more faintly, from St. Cuthbert's yonder on the other side of the Castle. Immediately the streets were filled with people hurrying to church. You didn't see them come out of the houses; they were just there of a sudden, all rushing along with set Sabbath expressions on their faces. Many of them were carrying umbrellas. How fast that fashion had caught on! It was only a matter of months since old Sandy Wood, the surgeon, appeared with the first one ever seen in Edinburgh. Walter had had a sight of it that first day; a huge gingham affair it was, and urchins had followed the kind old doctor throwing pebbles at it and jeering.

"You count the umbrellas on that side of the street,"

suggested Tom, "and I'll count them on this. The one that gets the most wins."

When they reached Greyfriars Walter would have liked to linger in the kirkyard till the service began. The Castle looked miles high from here, and today it was like a silhouette cut out of gray gauze and hung up against the sky. He wanted to show Mr. Mitchell the grave of Boswell of Auchinleck, on which the Covenant was signed. Mr. Mitchell would like that—he thought so highly of the Covenanters. But lingering was not permitted. They filed into the church and took their places, Walter contriving to slip into the coveted seat beside their mother, though Anne and Tom both wanted it. For a moment he was afraid that Anne was going to make a scene about it; her lower lip shot out dangerously and her breath came fast, but after a moment she subsided.

The church filled up quickly. Walter saw John Irving and his mother and sister come in; he saw, craning his neck, that his Uncle Daniel Rutherford was already there and his Aunt Christian, whom he called Miss Chritty because, being his mother's half-sister, she was young enough to take liberties with. He looked for Adam Ferguson and his father but could not see them. It was a long walk across the Meadows from their house on Sciennes Hill; maybe they would not come in the rain. Dr. Ferguson lived in terror of catching cold.

It was raining hard now, spattering against the windows. The church was dim and damp and smelled of

age and wet clothes. Robert came in just as the first
paraphrase was being given out. That was a narrow
squeak!

Dr. Erskine was going to preach today. Walter exchanged glances of satisfaction with his mother. He
knew she would be pleased. She liked Dr. Erskine's sermons very much better than Principal Robertson's, even
though he was the head of the University and the author
of some famous books.

Prayer followed paraphrase and psalm followed
prayer. Dr. Erskine gave out his text and Bibles fluttered all over the church. Walter followed the reading
of the text, closed his Bible and put it in the rack,
slipped down on the bench to the most comfortable
position he could find. Now for the long pull.

Dr. Erskine's face under his unpowdered black wig
looked very white. Hollow-chested and a little gaunt,
he propped himself up with a hand on either side of
the pulpit and launched into his sermon. Walter listened attentively to the main heads, and then he let his
mind wander.

Dr. Erskine's bands looked mussed. Probably he forgot to give them to his wife to be laundered. He was the
most absent-minded man in Edinburgh. That time he
bumped into a cow on Bruntsfield Links and took off
his hat and apologized! And the time he met his wife
in the Meadows and bowed to her and hoped she was
well and went on again, and then told her that evening
that he'd met a lady in the Meadows but couldn't for the
life of him imagine who she was!

That Green-Breeks following them down the Meadow Walk and making faces at them on their way to church! He wouldn't dare do that on a week-day. Maybe he would, though. He'd dare almost anything. They ought to get their banner out, the one Lady Elizabeth gave them before she went away to London. They hadn't used it for a long time, but probably Mother knew where it was. By jing, it would be a good thing to use against Green-Breeks and his callants.

Not that there would be so much time for bickers now with a tutor in the house. When they weren't at school they were to learn writing from him and arithmetic and French. He seemed pleasant enough, if he weren't so religious.

Walter suppressed a yawn and shifted a bit to ease his leg. Sitting still so long on the hard bench made it ache. He caught a fragment of the sermon and stowed it away in his memory. That would be a good one to get off when Father began asking questions. He heard Tom sigh gustily beside him.

That was Lady Anne Lindsay sitting next to Miss Chritty. He knew her right away though he had only seen her once before. She didn't usually come to Greyfriars. He knew a secret about her that many a one would give his ears to know. It was she who wrote "Auld Robin Gray," which everybody was singing and wondering who wrote the new words to the old tune. Miss Chritty told him about it, that day she took him to tea at Lady Balcarres's in Hyndford's Close and Lady Anne Lindsay, as calm and unconcerned as you please, sang

"Auld Robin Gray" to the harpsichord. There had been an embroidered screen behind her and a candle shedding light on the cloud of her hair; she looked so pretty and young, not at all like someone who could write a song that would set all Edinburgh to guessing and conjecturing.

Probably she didn't want it known who wrote it because the old words to that tune were so coarse and improper; anyhow it was not ladylike to write for the public. But man, wouldn't it be fun to write something that everybody was talking about and wondering who the author was—and not tell you wrote it!

Robert had written a poem. The night before the battle he wrote an elegy on the loss of the vessel—and then the next day was the fight and the ship wasn't lost at all. But it was a pretty fair poem. Something about "No more the geese shall cackle on the poop, No more the bagpipes through the orlop sound, De dum, de dum, de dum, de dum, In death's dark road at anchor fast they stay, De dum, de dum, something or other, *obey*."

His eyes glazed, his lips parted, and he slept.

He woke when the sermon was over and sat up very straight and wide-eyed, hoping that nobody had noticed his lapse.

When the congregation began flowing slowly out of church he maneuvered so as to get a word or two with Miss Chritty.

"How are all at your house?" she said.

"Oh, we're all looking very religious and very sour,"

he replied airily, glancing at her sidewise to see how she would take it. She smiled.

"You're looking a bit thin and peaked, yourself," she said. "You had better come over to our house and let Daniel see you."

He resolved mentally that he would do no such thing. He was of no mind to spend another week or so in bed, which seemed to be the outcome of almost every meeting he had had recently with his Uncle Daniel, who was professor of medicine at the University.

His mother was talking to Miss Chritty on the other side. "We have a tutor now," she was saying. "That is one step. The next will be to get them a music master. I should like them to know the Psalmody at least so that they can sing in church without hurting the ears of everyone around them."

On Sundays they dined "between sermons" instead of at the usual hour of three, in order to be back in church again for the second service at two o'clock. It hardly gave you time to stretch your legs, certainly not to regain your spirits, for Sunday dinner was a swift and somber meal. What conversation there was, was unrelievedly Calvinistic. And the day only half over!

Walter slept again during the afternoon service, and dozed over Rowe's *Letters,* which he was given to amuse himself with during the late afternoon hours after they reached home. John had Gesner's *Death of Abel* and Tom, Blair's *Sermons.* Anne was lucky; she drew *Pilgrim's Progress.* They read and yawned and sighed and looked yearningly at the windows, while Mr. Mitchell sat beside them with a book of his own and glanced at intervals over his spectacles to make sure that no levity or cheerfulness entered the scene.

The sun had come out and all the world on the other side of the windows was shining and glistening. Blackbirds sang in the back garden; the air was fragrant with flowering lilac; beyond the Meadows the Pentland Hills rose to touch a sky the color of harebells. A pity— "Waugh-oo," he yawned—to be shut up within doors when there was so much to see and do among the hills.

When twilight came on they were summoned to the drawing-room to be examined on the Catechism and the sermons. It was like church again. Mr. Mitchell acted as chaplain and began the session with a prayer, then Mr. Scott, elegantly pious in black knee-breeches and snowy ruffles, conducted the examination of his flock, while Mrs. Scott sat back in a corner, making no comments but following everything with her dark, heavy-lidded, all-seeing eyes.

Mr. Mitchell had rehearsed them the day before in their Catechism. He watched them now as nervously as if he, not they, were being tested. As each one finished he would settle back a moment, relieved, then stiffen up again when the next one began. He wore his own hair, unpowdered, and as his forehead perspired the hair curled up in little tendrils around the edge. He was a very earnest young man.

He is a Whig and I am a Tory, thought Walter. He is a Roundhead and I am a Cavalier. He likes Argyle and I like Montrose. We couldn't be any differenter.

There was a faint satisfaction in the thought. Mr. Mitchell was enthusiastic in defending his principles—Walter had led him on to talk about them yesterday when they were supposed to be studying arithmetic—but he could not shake Walter's secret conviction that the Cavalier side was the more gentlemanlike one to be on.

"Walter!"

"Yes, sir."

They had left the Catechism and were on the sermons. There was more fun in this, for he had every Sunday a wager with himself as to whether he could weave the bits of the sermon that he had heard between naps into a fabric that would satisfy his father.

He gave an excellent account of himself and sat down in a glow. John fared worse. He was in college now, and Mr. Scott, having heard rumors that the college was tainted with infidelity, was taking no chances. He made certain that John got everything that there was to be got from the services that day at Greyfriars. Nobody escaped. Even Robert, big as he was, had to make his recitation. Tom fumbled painfully for a glimmer of the truth, Anne said something sweet and vague, and some elementary sentiments were extracted with difficulty from Daniel.

The session was concluded with another prayer by Mr. Mitchell, and then Mrs. Scott rang for James to tell him they were ready for supper.

"It's almost over now," said John wearily.

"Wattie sleeps all the way through the sermons," grumbled Tom, "and then answers the questions better than anyone else."

It was true. He did. It was the only fun in the whole day, guessing what the minister would say. Of course he was always careful to listen for the main heads before he went to sleep. You had to have something to go on. But oh, if you could only get out and walk in the hills on a Sunday! Even if you had to keep to the paths.

A knock came at the front door.

"I'll go!" said Walter and Thomas in a breath.

When they saw who was standing on the doorstep with a black hat set athwart his wig and his coat falling to his knees, they fell on him with rapture and pulled him in. Mr. George Constable come for supper! The day was saved.

He was the only person who was permitted to turn the conversation on Sunday evenings to lighter subjects than original sin and predestination. He would take things into his own hands, and he would tell story after story of the '45 with his own dry biting humor until presently even Mr. Scott smiled and relaxed. The Sunday evening radishes and cheese and ale tasted entirely different when Mr. Constable was there. Even Walter's favorite Gruyère cheese tasted better.

GREEN-BREEKS

THE bicker, raging furiously, spilled out of the Square into the Meadows. Walter and Colin Mackenzie and Donald Gordon planted the banner on the top of some rising ground, and waves of Potterrow loons, with Green-Breeks always on the crest of them, swept up almost to it and then withdrew again for a fresh surge. Divots, sticks, stones flew through the air; there were howls and yells and shouts. Walter got a clod on the side of his face that scratched his cheek and filled his mouth with grass and dirt. A stone caught George Cumming in the arm. He doubled up in pain, clasping his arm tight in his other hand and making the most fearful grimaces to keep from crying out.

"I know something better than stones," shouted Tom angrily.

He was off toward the Square, calling back over his shoulder as he ran, "I'm going to get something. I'll be right back."

The enemy, seeing him go, gave a howl of delight and made a fresh charge.

"They're rinnin' awa'. They're frichtit!"

"Seize the banner," yelled Green-Breeks. "On, lads, and tear doon yon bit rag!"

Wiping the mud out of his eyes with a swipe of his arm Walter balanced a divot on the heel of his palm, took aim, and heaved it with all his strength at Green-Breeks's bare feet. Trip him up. The next instant he had to duck himself, and he heard a stone go whizzing past his ear. By jing, this was like a real battle. They were forcing them back now, even without Tom. Where had he gone? They couldn't spare anybody. Good. George was in the fray again, picking up divots as fast as they came and flinging them back with his left arm.

"A Gordon! A Gordon!" Donald shouted the battle cry of his clan and was off down the hill after a Potter-row loon that got left behind in the retreat. In another minute, though, he was scrambling back with Green-Breeks on his heels. The tide had turned again.

This time Walter missed his aim. Green-Breeks came bounding on, taking great leaps with his long legs, his yellow hair streaming out behind him. Before Walter could lift the standard and carry the banner to safety Green-Breeks had laid his hands on it.

Uproar and confusion. Shouting and roaring, both sides came rushing to the aid of their leaders, who struggled body to body in silent, panting combat. Missiles fell all around them. Walter shifted his hand to get a better grip on the standard, and in that instant Green-Breeks with a savage twist tore it away from him. Before he could run away with it a fresh voice shrilled above the din, something flashed in the air, and Green-Breeks dropped to the ground at Walter's feet. Amazed, he turned.

Tom was there behind him with Invernahyle's whinger in his upraised hand. Walter saw the exultation of the fight drain out of his face and a look of terror darken his eyes and whiten his lips. The whinger dropped from his nerveless hand. There was blood on it.

Walter looked down at Green-Breeks. He lay there as he had fallen, his eyes closed, blood seeping up from his forehead into his fair hair.

He heard gasping and heavy breathing as the others pressed close around the fallen lad. Nobody said a word. Suddenly, overwhelmed with horror and fright, they turned as one man—both sides—and ran for home.

Walter as usual was the last one. He went stumping along caught up in a flame of panic, with nothing in his mind—not Green-Breeks unconscious on the Meadow hillside, nor Thomas who cut him down—but his overwhelming need to get away from the place.

When they reached George Square, he met Tam Mac-Gregor the watchman going on his rounds, and he remembered Green-Breeks.

"There's a laddie down there," he had to stop and lick his dry lips before he could go on, "there's a laddie in the Meadows—hurt."

"Where?"

He pointed with a shaking hand.

"Aye. I'll see tae him. I doubt ye've killed somebody in yer bickers. I always thocht ye would—sticks and stanes and—"

Walter did not stay to hear any more.

He found Tom in their room, crouched at the foot of the bed in utter misery and terror. He raised an ashen face when Walter came in.

"Wattie, will he die?"

Walter thought of the watchman's words and a shudder shook him from head to foot.

"I don't know," he whispered.

"Will—will they try me in the court?"

"Maybe he's no dead. Maybe's he's just got a sair dunt on the head." His mother had said something like that once, when he first got the whinger. What would his mother say when she knew what had happened?

"Lord Braxfield, Wattie?"

Walter thought of Lord Braxfield, the most terrible of the judges. "Aye, ye're a clever chiel," he was said to have said once to a prisoner who had made a strong plea for his life, "but ye wad be nane the waur o' a hanging."

"No, no," he said, "Father would save you from him."

But could he? And what would he say when he knew? He would be disgraced among his fellows. He a Writer to the Signet, and his son a—— "Maybe he's just got a dunt on the head," he repeated forlornly.

"I never meant to hurt him—I just wanted to make him let go of the banner. I thought the whinger would make it more like a real battle, but I wasn't really going to use it. I wish I'd never touched the old thing——"

The whinger. It was down there in the Meadows now. Anybody would know whose it was.

"We'd best go and get it."

They crept down the stairs and out into the Square. Dusk was drawing in, and every bush held shadows that seemed ready to spring out on them and denounce them. The Meadows looked wild and lonely. Arthur's Seat leaned against a pale-green sky and a cloud was silvered at the edges by the moon behind it. They saw nobody until they reached the place where Green-Breeks had been. Colin Mackenzie and Lordie Ramsay were sitting there white-faced and drawn, pulling blades of grass through their fingers and saying nothing. Green-Breeks was gone and the blood-stained whinger was lying in the grass where it had fallen.

"Have ye heard anything?"

They shook their heads.

"It's a terrible business," said Colin, "a terrible business."

Tom's chin trembled and he bit his lower lip.

"Doesn't anybody know," said Walter hoarsely, "how Green-Breeks is?" He felt that he could not bear it unless he found out.

Three more boys joined them, drifting out of the shadows. They had no news either. Miserable, they hoped the others had. They did not know whom to ask. Tam MacGregor had not come round again; the servants would only make more trouble by talking; and there would be a terrible pother when the parents learned about it. They were so set against bickers anyhow. Everyone agreed that it must be kept from the parents as long as possible.

"Where would they take him?"

"The Infirmary, I'd think."

"Somebody could go to the Infirmary door and spier."

"Yes—and anyone who went would be nabbed for doing it."

"He could say he didn't."

"They'd know he knew something about it."

"Man, I wouldn't be in your shoes," said Donald to Tom.

"We're all in it together," retorted Walter stoutly. "Tom cut him down, but it was my whinger and we were all in the bicker."

"What we must do," said Colin suddenly, "is to promise, all of us, not to tell anything about it."

"Green-Breeks would know."

"Tam MacGregor will be suspecting."

"We'll have to chance that. Where's the whinger?"

"Here it is."

"Bury it."

"Throw it in the ditch and cover it with leaves and grass."

Walter felt guilty and shabby. His heroes would have stepped forth boldly and said, "I did it"; they would have taken the consequences without a murmur. But he hadn't done it. Tom had. And Tom was stricken with remorse and terror beyond all bounds—you had to feel sorry for him. You had to do what you could to get him out of the mess. Sir Galahad in the same situation would have taken his brother's sin upon himself, but Sir Galahad would have been pretty sure of getting cleared in the end; ordinary folk weren't always so lucky. It would be terrible to be branded always for something you had not done. And after all, the harm was done to Green-Breeks now; it wouldn't make him any better or any worse whether Tom got found out or not. The first thing was to hide the whinger where nobody would ever find it. Besides it was his whinger. Anybody who found it would think he did it, and while he might contemplate nobly confessing to Tom's fault as his own, he had no intention at all of allowing himself to be wrongly accused of it.

"The ditch is the place—way down there under the big tree."

They buried it deep, touching it with dread and revulsion.

"Now," said Colin, still in command, "we must all pile our hands up together over the place where it is hidden and swear to keep the secret."

They gathered in a circle, leaning over the ditch in the deep shadow of a big lime tree and stacked their right hands one above the other. Walter made up the oath.

"I solemnly swear," they said in turn, "by the blood-stained whinger that lies buried here, never to reveal to a living soul who cut Green-Breeks down."

Moonlight glimmered faintly on the grass; the wind rustled in the tree above their heads. In the houses in

George Square there were lights, and beyond and above them in the tall "lands" of the High Street more lights twinkled, almost in the sky it seemed.

"We'll be late for supper," someone said.

It was a normal thought that somehow gave them comfort, and they set off in a great hurry. Tom and Wattie followed slowly, dread and fear clamping down like an iron lid on their hearts. If they only knew how Green-Breeks was, even if they knew the worst.

"I don't want any supper, Wattie."

"I don't either, but they'll know something's wrong if we don't eat." To act as usual, to pretend to be carefree, that was the price you paid for secrecy.

"I liked Green-Breeks."

"It may be just a sair dunt on the head. We'll find out in the morning." (The Town Guard knocking on the door before they were awake, maybe, to take Tom away to the Tolbooth.)

For the first time in their lives they could not sleep, and the night was endless and horror-ridden.

CONSEQUENCES

ARLY in the morning Wattie remembered the banner. Nobody had given it a thought last night. Somebody must have got it because it certainly was not there when they all met in the Meadows in the twilight, but who could have taken it? Well, that was just one thing more to worry about.

There was comment at breakfast upon their heavy eyes and lack of appetite. Mrs. Scott put her hand on Walter's forehead.

"Wattie, you have a touch of fever again. I don't like his looks, Mr. Scott. Do ye no think he'd best stay away from the school?"

"No, Mother, please. I'd rather go to school." The Infirmary was next door to the High School, and he could surely find out something about Green-Breeks there. "I really can't afford to lose any more school now."

"Mr. Mitchell can hear you your lessons, since you're so studious of a sudden. You too, Thomas—no, you've no fever. Put out your tongue."

"Likely they've been stuffing gingerbread at Lucky Fykie's," said John superiorly.

"I have not. I'm saving my money for a book of ballads."

"It's the summer weather. You make mollycoddles of the lads, Anne. They'll be all right when the vacation comes and they go to Kelso, eh, Walter?"

Walter smiled, with an effort. Even the prospect of going to visit Aunt Janet, who had been living at Kelso since Grandmother died, failed to cheer him this morning. All he could think of now was of getting through and finding out about Green-Breeks.

"Please, may I be excused? I don't wish to be late."

His parents exchanged puzzled and troubled glances but let him go. Tom followed close on his heels.

In the Square they found Tam MacGregor. He looked up and down to make sure nobody was watching before he motioned with his head for them to follow him into the shelter of an area way.

"Here," he said, pulling a folded wad of silk out of his pocket, "here's your banner. I tossed the staff away yonder in the Meadows."

"Tam, is Green-Breeks dead?"

"Na, na, he's no deid—sma' thanks to the George Square laddies and their bickers. He was unconscious when I carried him to the Infirmary, but he came to himsel' before I left."

Wattie drew a long breath. He had known all the time it was just a dunt on the head.

"Did he—say anything?" inquired Tom diffidently.

"No, he was too dazed-like. And I didna say onything mysel'. They spiered me hoo it happened and I told them I didna ken onything but juist that I'd found him in the Meadows."

"Thank ye, Tam. *Thank* ye. Nobody meant to hurt him."

"Och, I unnerstand. I suppose the chiel that threw the stone thocht it wad turrn tae porridge in the air. Noo, let this be a lesson tae ye. Bickers is rough games. Aweel, awa' wi' ye."

They were almost late for school after all. During prayers in the Long Hall, Walter sat in a sort of cloud of relief. It was all right. Green-Breeks was not going to die. He had never really thought he would of course, but it was good to know for sure. And Tom was safe. They were all safe.

Unless, of course, he thought on the way up the turn-pike stairs, Green-Breeks when he got over being dazed should remember who had hit him and come out with it. There would be a pretty kettle of fish. Tom would be flogged, of course, and maybe they both would be kept home from Kelso; worst of all, bickers would be forbidden. And what the Potterrow lads wouldn't do when they found out that the George Square boys were forbidden to fight! They would be laughed to scorn abroad if they didn't and thrashed at home if they did.

No, they weren't out of the woods yet.

"What's wrong wi' you?" inquired Irving solicitously. "You look down in the mouth."

"I'm sleepy."

He wasn't, though. Strange that you could stay awake through a whole night and not be sleepy the next day.

He was tense, his back and leg ached, and he felt dread-fully old and battered, but he was not sleepy.

When the play hour came, instead of going to Lucky Brown's for jube, he drifted up the Wynd and looked at the Infirmary. Now and then he could see somebody go past a window inside, but nothing more.

Adam Ferguson sauntered up, eating bramble pie as he came and leaning forward to keep the juice from dripping down his front.

"Want some?"

"No, thanks. Look you, go up to the Infirmary door and ask how is the lad that got carried in hurt last night."

"Why don't you do it yourself?"

"I don't want to."

"Who is it that's hurt?"

"Green-Breeks."

"Was't you that hurt him?"

"No."

"Ye might tell me about it if I'm to go."

"I swore not to reveal it to a living soul."

"Oh." Adam licked his fingers. "All right."

He went off and in a few minutes he came back full of news.

"They say he's better and he'll be out the morn or the morn's morn at the latest. They asked me and asked me did I know how he got hurt. They say he's had a terrible blow on the head and they would like fine to get their hands on the one that did it."

"Won't he tell them?"

"No. They say he knows but he's determined not to tell. Wattie, if you tell me I won't breathe it to a living soul."

But Walter was already hurrying to find Tom and relay the good news to him. He went back to his classes feeling a great admiration for Green-Breeks. By jing, he was just a bare-shanked lad from the Potterrow, but he was acting as Sir Nigel might have acted. They would have to make it up to him, that's what they'd have to do.

The next day was Wednesday, and the boys spent their half-holiday in a remote and hidden glen between the Braid and the Blackford Hills. In the course of the afternoon the George Square lads withdrew from the rest to a cave in the hill that had been used as a refuge in Covenanting times and there, squatting around in a circle, they considered the question of a suitable reward for Green-Breeks.

They agreed that something must be done. It was felt that a silver watch, appropriately inscribed, would be just the thing, and for a moment or two they glowed with appreciation of Green-Breeks's nobility and their own generosity. It was necessary, however, to be practical. Somebody suggested a suit of clothes—"But then he wouldn't be Green-Breeks," protested Walter, "and anyhow that's a daft gift"—and somebody else a wallet. Wattie thought a book would be good. George Cumming said slyly, "He might like a whinger," and the cave echoed with whoops of laughter.

"Let's just give him the money," said Tom sensibly. "Then he can buy himself whatever he wants."

That idea suited everybody and the meeting was about to break up when Colin said, almost as an afterthought, "What money?"

So they had to begin again. Well, Wattie said, he and Tom must give the most. He had the money he was saving to buy Langhorne's *Poems,* and Tom had a few pennies and thought he could get John to pay back sixpence he had borrowed. The others promised to contribute what they could.

Irving and Adam and Davy Douglas began to make rude noises outside the cave, threatening to come in and learn all the secrets, which they promised to reveal immediately to Dr. Adam, Lord Braxfield, Mr. Scott, and King George.

"We'll give the money to Wattie and he can take it to Green-Breeks with our deep appreciation and so forth—he'd do it best," said Donald, and was out of the cave in a rush, butting into Adam and rolling him down the slope.

Wattie found that he had no easy task, even after the money finally was collected. Green-Breeks, though he was out of the Infirmary, was not to be found. Evidently he was still not feeling very well and was staying within doors. Walter knew where he lived, but he couldn't get near the house, for every time he appeared in the Potter-row, Green-Breeks's henchmen fell upon him and in spite of his protestations and his flag of truce, ran him out of the street. He decided at last to approach him through their mutual friend, Lucky Fykie.

Lucky Fykie's shop, where the lads went for gingerbread and lollypops and their elders for anything from onions to cotton wicks and from a whip-shaft to a glass of brandy, was a very different sort of place from Lucky Brown's establishment. Lucky Fykie was an old, old lady, very neat and select. She sold her assorted articles as if her left hand did not know that her right hand was demeaning itself by taking money for them. Every day at the time when the lawyers would be coming home from the Court, she would put out on the bunker seat of the window a row of bottles containing whisky, rum, and brandy, a salver of glasses and a plate of ginger-bread biscuits. Elderly gentlemen would drop in, bow, say "How d'you do, mem?" help themselves, bow once more, and go out. Nothing embarrassing was ever said about payment; it was as if they were privileged to enjoy her hospitality. Once a month or so they would approach her privately at an odd hour and settle up.

Walter thought he had chosen a time to talk with Lucky Fykie when no one else was likely to be there—in fact, he played truant from school for that very pur-pose—but he had hardly got well launched on the ex-planation of his errand when the door opened and in walked—of all people!—his father. He had just time to dive under the counter. If his father should happen to glance down he must inevitably be discovered, but he had no chance to seek a safer hiding-place. He crouched with his cheek against his knee and waited.

Mr. Scott had chosen this most inopportune moment to pay his score with Lucky Fykie. There was a little murmuring about the number of glasses, a faint clink of silver, and then Mr. Scott said "Good day to you, mem," and departed, the very figure of a dignified gentleman who has accomplished a delicate transaction in a genteel way—without the least idea that his son was eying his legs from beneath the very counter on which he had left, as if absent-mindedly, his silver coins.

When he had gone, Walter emerged, unabashed.

"As I was saying——"

He left the package of coppers with Lucky Fykie, who promised to give them to Green-Breeks together with as much of Walter's speech of presentation as she could remember. He was to come back the next evening to hear how it had been received.

When he returned, the old lady told him,

"He said to thenk ye very kindly, but he wadna tak' the money. He said he wouldna tell anyhow, for that wad be clam."

Wattie clapped his fist into his palm. By jing, this barefoot Green-Breeks was a gentleman. He had acted better than any of them. Blushing for their mistake in offering him money, Walter made an effort to imagine how he himself would feel in the circumstances and after a moment brought out hesitantly,

"Maybe there's some bit giftie we could give the old woman he lives with."

"She likes snuff," suggested Lucky Fykie. "He comes in whiles to buy her a poke."

Walter bought a whole pound of snuff and begged that Green-Breeks would accept it as a slight token of their continued and increased appreciation. The next day Lucky Fykie reported that Green-Breeks had taken the snuff to his grand-dame and that they were both well pleased with it.

A few days later, Walter, returning late to George Square—he had been having a crack with Mrs. Cockburn in Crichton Street—heard the unmistakable noises of a bicker. He quickened his pace.

When he came round the corner the first person he saw was Green-Breeks, looking quite himself again, his aim and energy apparently unimpaired. He shouted "Truce! Truce!" and came running up to Walter.

"I've no hard feeling," he said, half apologetically, "but bickers are graund sport. It wad be a peety to gi'e them up, would it no?"

He put out his hand and Walter shook it warmly. Yes, this was best. They might have become friends, but they were of different stations, and the bickers *were* fun. They would remain chivalrous enemies. So might two knights have done when they found foemen worthy of their steel.

"I have the highest respect for you," he said heartily.

"I like you fine mysel'," replied Green-Breeks.

They parted. The truce was at an end.

"No stones!" cried Wattie.

"No stones!" Green-Breeks took it up.

It had rained earlier in the day and the ground was soft. Wattie caught up a wet clod and took aim. He noted with satisfaction that it landed bang in the middle of Green-Breeks's chest.

12

THE POET

WALTER limped to his place in the Rector's class and sat down. He was ninth. There were one hundred and seven boys behind him. He did not know just how it had happened, but Latin as Dr. Adam taught it seemed to be easier and more interesting, and he had mounted to the first form almost before he knew where he was. Now that he was here he was going to take good care to stay. He had a reputation to maintain now. The Rector had said of him,

"Many of the lads understand the *Latin* better, but Gualterus Scott is behind few in following and enjoying the author's *meaning*."

James Buchan was *dux*. He had kept first place ever since Wattie had been coming to the High School. No use trying to dislodge him. Ninth was good enough. Ninth, or maybe eighth.

Dr. Adam came in with his gown billowing out behind him, his cheeks red and his hair slightly ruffled by the wind, and sat down at his desk on the platform. For a moment his thin fine hands were busy among his papers and piles of books, then he looked up and gazed out benignly over his flock.

Walter's breath quickened, he felt the class behind him stir attentively. Today was the day.

"Yes," pronounced the Rector, "I have read your verses, the verses of those of you who were interested enough to make this additional effort. I think you will find when you grow older that no effort which you put into your school work ever fails to bear fruit far beyond the due and fit but still puerile rewards of the classroom. I have been teaching boys since I was a young man of nineteen and I am acquainted with the subsequent history of every lad who has passed under my tutelage, and I say to you that I could have prophesied in advance what their several fates would be, for invariably those who were diligent in school have prospered in after life and those who were idle and inattentive in their lessons have failed signally in the greater tasks of life."

The good doctor was off on his hobbyhorse. He would go on until he felt the attention of the lads slacken and then he would switch abruptly back to the matter in hand. His wise gray eyes with the twinkle at the corners saw every shade of expression that passed over their faces.

"I have read your papers carefully, in which you have turned passages of Vergil into English verse, and I have chosen two, one to receive the prize and one to receive honorable mention."

Now was the moment.

"The prize is awarded to Colin Mackenzie for Dido's

speech. After I have read the piece, the author of it will please step forward to the platform."

He read the poem carefully, with the kinds of emphasis necessary to make the meter come out right, and Walter said to himself judicially that it was very fine indeed. He wouldn't have thought old Colin had it in him.

He looked very handsome when he went up to receive his prize, which all, craning their necks, perceived at once to be nothing but a calendar. His face, pale from excitement, was in striking contrast to his dark eyes and dark hair; he was tall and slender and even in his school clothes he had a look of elegance.

As he climbed over Wattie to get back to his place, Walter gave him a congratulatory thump on the shoulder.

The Rector picked up another sheet of paper.

"Gualterus Scott receives honorable mention for a description of Mount Ætna: .

"In awful ruins Ætna thunders high,
    And sends in pitchy whirlwinds to the sky
    Black clouds of smoke . . ."

Wattie felt silly, sitting there while his poem was being read out. His face flamed and his fingers were damp in his pockets. And yet, deep in his heart was a solid core of contentment. Never before had anything sounded quite so good in his ears.

". . . The stones made liquid as the huge mass flies,

(The end was almost reached now)

"Then back again with greater weight recoils
While Ætna thundering from the bottom boils."

He limped forward and received his paper and a
handshake from the Rector. The class clapped and
stamped—more, he felt, because they seized any excuse
for making a racket than because they wished to pay
honest tribute to literary achievement—until they were
peremptorily ordered to cease.

He presented the poem to his mother that evening.
After she had read it over twice and commented on its
merits, she wrote on it "My Walter's first lines, 1782"
and put it away carefully in a drawer in her secretary.

"Why'd you write that?" he asked curiously.

"Because I think they'll not be your last. These were
a translation. One of these days you'll be writing something out of your own head. But, Wattie," she added,
"your handwriting is nothing short of a disgrace. It is
no more than a scrawl. What d'you do when Mr. Mitchell is teaching you writing—lure him into discussing
the Cavaliers the whole hour?"

Early in the new year when the joys and excitements
of Hogmanay were past, and the weather, with sleet
and snow and slush and a snell wind off the Firth, made
it desirable to stay within doors, Wattie wrote another
poem and tasted fame once more. A headier draught
this time, for there was no Colin Mackenzie involved,
to get the greater part of the glory. He wrote a description of a thunderstorm, with a neat moral sentiment in
the tail of it.

Dr. Adam praised it and mentioned it with approval to Mrs. Scott when he saw her after church. Mrs. Cockburn was all enthusiasm. Uncle Daniel Rutherford and Miss Chritty were equally, though more reservedly, impressed. Mr. George Constable presented him with a shilling on the strength of it, and when he went into the apothecary's shop to spend a part of it on horehound drops, one of the university students who boarded at the house of the poet Blacklock said to him, "I hear you've written a poem."

"Oh, it's nothing," said Walter modestly, but could not refrain from adding, "How did you know?"

"Your brother John said something about it. How does it go?"

"I couldn't recite it, but if you've got a bit of paper I'll write it out for you."

He borrowed a quill from the apothecary and wrote it out. The student read it and passed it to the apothecary, who read it and handed it on to his wife.

"I'm on my way home now," said the student. "Come along with me and I'll introduce you to Dr. Blacklock."

If Walter had had time to think he might have demurred out of shyness, for blind Dr. Blacklock was Edinburgh's most famous poet—in fact he was the only poet north of the Severn—and his home was frequented by the city's leading lights. Dr. Hume went there often for tea, and the Duchess of Gordon, and Lord Monboddo and his beautiful daughter Miss Bess Burnett, and many another shining one. He had often seen the blind poet being led through the streets by one or another of his devoted disciples, but he had never imagined that he himself would be invited to the poet's house. When they reached the door they heard music coming faintly and sweetly from within.

"His flageolet," explained the student. "He plays it when he's feeling depressed. That's his famous 'Pastoral Song' he's playing now."

They went in. The room was dimly lit by a fire that had dwindled to coals, but it was light enough for the woman who sat knitting near the window and the gentle, white-haired old man who, when he heard the unfamiliar footsteps, slipped his flageolet into his pocket and looked inquiringly toward the door. His face, which was pitted with the smallpox that had cost him his sight, was kind and almost gay in expression. Something about that hopeful, defenseless gaze struck at Walter's heart.

"I've brought you young Walter Scott," said the student. "He's by way of being a poet too—perhaps you can persuade him to recite his verses to you."

"I am glad, I am very glad. Now we shall not be alone for tea. The weather has been so dull today that no one has ventured out to see us."

Walter limped across the room to take the hand that groped toward him; it felt very thin and fragile in his own strong one. Then, blushing to think that he had left the lady to the last, he turned and paid his respects to Mrs. Blacklock.

"His footsteps—is the lad lame?"

"Yes, but he gets about everywhere."

"We are well met, my son—two poets, one blind and

one lame. But I am old and you are young, and you get about everywhere. Now let me hear your verses."

A little huskily Walter repeated his poem, glancing about him at the little room as he did so. That he, Walter Scott, was talking to a real poet!

"That's very fine, very fine indeed. You must continue to court the Muse. Now, Mrs. Blacklock, if you will give us some tea—and while she is fetching it, what shall we talk about?"

"You were playing, sir, when we came in——"

"Ah yes, my flageolet. A great joy to me. Its use was suggested to me in a dream."

Out it came from his pocket, and he played his "Pastoral Song" again.

When tea came in, he was reminded of the time the great Dr. Johnson came to call upon him.

"It was in the summer of 1773, and he was stopping with Mr. Boswell in James's Court. I went first to wait upon him as was proper, and the next day—I took it very courteous of him to be so prompt—he returned my visit. We had a very edifying conversation and he drank nineteen cups of tea—to my wife's consternation."

"I have never seen such a man," declared Mrs. Blacklock. "To be sure, he is enormous, but one wad never think that even he could hold it all. I don't see that he is so great. He has written a dictionary, true enough, but then Dr. Blacklock is a contributor to the *Encyclopædia Britannica*."

"Only one article, my dear, and that on a subject I am peculiarly fitted to handle—the blind. Do you like

to read, young Walter Scott? If you do, and you lack
for books, you may borrow any of mine that you like.
There's Ossian there, and Spenser—d'you know Spenser?"

When Walter went home he was walking on air, with
the *Faerie Queene* under his arm. (Dr. Blacklock had as-
sured him that it had more knights and giants and
dragons than queens in it.) He had had tea with Dr. Blacklock! His poem had been praised! He had a new book to
read and when he finished it he could go back and get
more. His cup was full.

This exalted mood lasted exactly until he reached
George Square. There he met John, who had news that
reduced him in one instant to rage and despair.

"Look here, Wattie," said John, "did you show the
apothecary's wife your poem?"

"Well, I didn't exactly show it to her myself, but she
saw it. Why?"

"She did? I told Wullie she could not possibly have
seen it. She's telling everybody she saw the same thing
in an old magazine and that you must have copied it."

Walter all but choked. The apothecary's wife. A blue-
buskined apothecary's wife saying that he had stolen his
poem from an old magazine. How dared she!

"How d'you know she's saying that?"

"She told Wullie Edmonstone and he told me just
now."

"Here, you take this home for me." Walter thrust
his book at John.

"Where are you going?"

"I'm going to see that apothecary's wife."

"It's supper time now. Wait till afterwards and I'll
go with you."

"I can't wait."

His honor was at stake.

Smarting with injustice and hot with anger he made
better time through the dark streets than ever he had
made even in a bicker. Here and there a flickering street
lamp made a faint pool of light under the tall black
buildings; a torchbearer went ahead of a sedan chair,
his light footsteps and the chairmen's heavier ones echo-
ing on the stone pavement; the door of a howff opened
and for a moment light and noise spilled out into the
street.

The apothecary's wife was at supper. Wattie per-
suaded the apprentice in the shop that the occasion was
serious enough to warrant calling her forth.

"Oh, so it's you. Well, what d'you want so urgently?"

"I hear that you are telling folk that I copied my poem
from an old magazine."

"Tuts, and you call me away from my supper for
that!"

"Did ye say it?"

"Ou, aye, I said it. And did ye no do it?"

"You know I didn't. You know it wasn't true."

"Be careful hoo ye say I lee. I juist said in passing to
a young gentleman that I'd seen the same poem in an
aul' number of the *Scots Toon and Country*."

"Where is it? Show it to me."

"There's the pile of magazines over there in the

corner. Go through them yoursel' if ye like. I'm getting back to my supper. Dinna look sae stricken, laddie. It's no great crime if ye did. I spoke withoot thinking——"

"But I *didn't*."

He flung himself on the magazines and went through them frantically. There were poems on Nature by the dozen and even poems on thunderstorms, but his was not there. How could it be?

The apothecary's wife had gone back to her supper. He dropped the last magazine on the pile hopelessly. What did it prove, his going through them? He knew it wouldn't be there. If he could make her look through them all and then admit that she had been wrong—— By jing, there was such a thing as libel! There was slander. There was defamation of character. He'd hale her into court. He'd make her admit she lied about his poem.

The apprentice looked at him owlishly from behind a glass jar containing some doleful purple liquid. "Best forget it," he said. "Forget it, that's the thing. The least said is the soonest mended."

Walter went out and slammed the door.

On the way home he met John, who had been sent by their mother to fetch him.

"Nobody will pay any attention to her," said John in a clumsy attempt at comforting.

"Wullie did," Walter pointed out.

Mrs. Scott had had some supper saved for him, and she sat with him while he ate it.

"Of course you wrote it yourself!" she exclaimed.

"Anybody that knows you knows you wouldn't pass off somebody else's poem for your own. Where is your poem? Let's read it over together."

He pulled the crumpled bit of paper out of his pocket and handed it to her between thumb and forefinger as if it hurt to touch it. He hated the sight of it.

> Loud o'er my head though awful thunders roll
> And vivid lightnings flash from pole to pole,
> Yet 'tis thy voice, my God, that bids them fly,
> Thy arm directs those lightnings through the sky.
> Then let the good thy mighty name revere
> And hardened sinners thy just vengeance fear.

"It is a very good poem and a very true one. The apothecary's wife was very hasty and she had no right to be saying something that she was not sure of. But do you know, Wattie, my lamb, I can see why she thought she had read it somewhere before?"

"Why?"

"It is a bit like a good many other poems. It's not that you copied it, for well I know you didn't; it's just that the sentiments and expressions have been used by other folk before you. It isn't what you really thought yourself. Your mind is not much on 'just vengeance'—it's chock-full of knights and tournaments. Next time you write a poem, you write about your knights."

"I'm not going to write a poem again," said Wattie fiercely. "Never."

His mother said nothing and cut him another piece of cake.

13

PARTINGS

WALTER rose from the breakfast table comfortably full of collops and tea. Yesterday morning he had snatched at a few hasty mouthfuls and rushed off to school with Thomas and Daniel. Yesterday he had been still a High School lad.

He strolled to the window and looked out at the back garden in its spring green and the Meadows beyond, where sunlight through the trees made splashes on the grass. Faintly he heard the sound of drums. By jing, the Twelfth Fusileers would be drilling today! He usually missed them because he was in school. He caught a glimpse of scarlet and heard the pipes now as well as the drums. He could see them better outdoors.

"Look out, Anne. Get out of my way. I'm in a hurry——"

"Wattie, come back here." His mother's voice pulled him up at the door. "You've no time to be off watching the soldiers. You must do your errands and get back in time——" She nodded significantly at Mr. Mitchell, who stood by the table polishing his spectacles.

Walter nodded back to show he understood, drew the

corners of his mouth down and went through the motions of shaking hands in a lingering and regretful manner, until suddenly he realized that Mr. Mitchell had put his spectacles back on his nose again and was looking at him with a mildly puzzled expression. Walter made another dash for the door.

"*Wattie!*"

Back once more. "Yes, Mother."

"Don't forget that note that your father wishes you to take to Mr. Wauchope."

"Four things: the note to Mr. Wauchope, the coach to Kelso, return the book to Dr. Blacklock, say good-by to Uncle Daniel and Miss Chritty."

"Oh. Then you were planning to go to Kelso without taking your Aunt Janet the cap she asked me to order for her?"

"Five things. Number five is the parcel for Miss Janet Scott from the milliner."

"Which milliner?"

"Elspeth Mackie on Princes Street."

"Don't forget that, of all things. Don't forget any of them. Now use your head, Wattie. Go first to Lucky Boyd's and make sure of your place in the coach, for if you don't get it you'll have to wait another week to go. And then take the note to Mr. Wauchope and get the cap while you're over in the New Town. Mind what I'm telling you, Wattie—anybody might think you'd never seen soldiers before—put the note in one pocket and the money for the cap in the other and then keep your hands out of them. Are your pockets clean? You can stop

in Hyndford's Close on the way back—and tell your
Uncle Daniel I would be glad to have his opinion about
this new Dr. Graham we hear so much of. I think you
had better not take the book to Dr. Blacklock till after
dinner. If you get to cracking with him you will never
remember to come home in time."

"Is that all?"

"Yes. Away with you now."

As he went through the door he heard his mother saying to Mr. Mitchell: "The lads are so different. Now
John would liefer die than be seen on Princes Street
with his aunt's cap in a parcel, but it doesn't trouble
Wattie at all."

Nothing troubled Wattie this morning. He glanced
over his shoulder at the Pentlands as he came out into
the Square. The Pentlands! What were they? Tomorrow he would be seeing the Cheviots. A blackbird was
singing its head off in the shrubbery—and what were
blackbirds? Tomorrow he would be seeing heron!

He supposed he might as well go to Lucky Boyd's first,
since his mother had suggested it, though there really
was no need to go at all. He had arranged a week ago
for the seat beside the driver on top of the coach. It was
the first thing he had done when he heard the good news.
Instead of finishing the spring term at the High School
he was to go to Kelso and spend the whole summer with
Aunt Jenny. None of your measly little fortnight visits,
but a whole summer in the border country. He'd be
there for the broom and the roses—and the strawberries
and raspberries, too.

" 'Oh the broom,' " he warbled, " 'the bonny bonny broom, The broom of Cowdenknowes.' "

He knew he was off the tune. For all Mr. Campbell's efforts he still could not carry a tune. Twice a week the music master came to teach them to sing, and they were all hopeless. Funny: Robert could sing and their father played the 'cello at the gentlemen's concerts, but the rest of them had not a note of music in their make-up. All that had come of the singing lessons was a note from Lady Cummings next door asking that the lads should not all be flogged at once, that she had no doubt they deserved it but the noise of the concord was really dreadful. They all thought it a grand joke and received it in high good humor, but poor Mr. Campbell was much mortified and Mrs. Scott began to despair of their ever learning the Psalmody so they would do her credit in church.

"He tuned his pipe and reed sae sweet
The birds stood listening by——"

When he came home from Kelso he would go into the college. Some of the lads were going to stay on for an additional year with Dr. Adam but Father thought it would be better for him to go on into college. He would be twelve and there were plenty more as young. He was to be a lawyer.

"E'en the dull cattle stood and gazed,
Charmed with his melody."

Robert was in the King's navy and John would go into the army. Walter was a lamiter and he would be a law-yer. Oh, well, why fret about that now. Let sorrow come when sorrow maun. Good things did happen un-expectedly. Here he had been ailing and miserable all spring on account of outgrowing his strength, and now he was going to Kelso.

"Oh the broom, the bonny, bonny broom!"

He would have some lessons with Mr. Whale, but they would not last long. The rest of the day he would be free to fish in the Tweed and explore the ruins of Kelso Ab-bey and Roxburgh Castle where James II was killed by his own cannon. Evenings there would be the cottage drawing-room and Aunt Janet and Cousin Barbara Scott reading and knitting and talking. It would be *good* to see Aunt Jenny again.

He stopped at the inn and made sure of his place in the coach. He had been in so often during the last week that they all knew him there. Andrew the groom showed him the new coach that was to be put on the Glasgow line, a gorgeous affair of green picked out in red, with yellow wheels. He climbed all over it, admir-ing the color and the fittings, the springs and the decora-tions on the panel. He was hoping that a coach would come in while he was there—he liked to see the inn-yard spring to life with running here and there by servants and grooms and onlookers, to see the horses steaming and rattling their harness as they tossed their heads, to watch the passengers descend, stiff and tired, but with that traveled look about them that came as much from the determined way they wore their hats pulled down over their eyes as from their travelers' paraphernalia of umbrella, boots, and bundles.

But no coach came in. There was just the shining, empty Glasgow coach in one corner, and the boys splashing pails of water over the cobblestones in the yard, and now and then the head of a maid-servant in a mobcap looking idly out of an upstairs window. Reluctantly he went on his way again, up St. Mary's Wynd and then to the left up the Canongate until he came to the North Bridge.

Two wagonloads of furniture passed him, with legs of chairs sticking up into the air and tables balanced on top of sofas. Everybody, it seemed, was moving into the New Town, away from their old mansions in the Canongate and the High Street. Princes Street was half built up already and there was talk of putting the new assembly rooms in George Street. He rested his arms on the balustrade of the bridge and looked up the valley toward the Earthen Mound. All that earth, cartload after cartload of it, thrown out when they dug the foundations of the houses in the New Town. That showed how many houses had been built already! Geordie Boyd's Mud Brig, people called it scornfully at first, but now it was the Earthen Mound and a regular passageway between the old and new towns. He would come back that way.

He'd better hurry! Mr. Mitchell was leaving at eleven. He was going to ride to Bo'ness today, spending the night on his sister's farm near there and going on his way tomorrow to Arbroath, where his new church was situated.

Everything was happening at once. Walter going to Kelso, and Mr. Mitchell leaving. Well, a minister was what he had always wanted to be. Nobody but Walter and Anne would be there to see him go—and Mother of course. That was too bad. He had been with them a year and they all liked him. It seemed forlorn for him to go off without everybody there to make a ceremony of it. It would have been a civil thing to give him a farewell present. Of course it was not too late yet, but what could it be? Walter had no money. He very earnestly hoped that his father would give him some spending money to take with him to Kelso, but so far it had not been forthcoming. There ought to be something he already had that he could give Mr. Mitchell. Probably he would like a book best. But which one? He considered it a sin to look at a play or a poem, even on a week day.

By jing, they were right when they said Princes Street was a fine street. It was built up on only one side; on the other you looked over a grassy hollow to the Old Town stretched along the ridge above you with the Castle at one end jutting up into the sky. The view of the Castle from Mr. Wauchope's door was splendid; the rock looked immense.

He gave the note to the servant and returned to the

little line of shops for Aunt Jenny's cap. Back he trudged to the Old Town over the Earthen Mound and up the steps by Allan Ramsay's house to the Lawnmarket. He paused to rest his leg, and St. Giles pealed out. Half-past ten! He would have to leave Uncle Daniel and Miss Chritty till the afternoon.

It was strange to be out in the middle of the morning when all the other lads were in school poring over their Adam's *Grammar*. Adam's *Grammar!* There was an idea. He could give his copy to Mr. Mitchell for a farewell present. He was always saying what an excellent work it was, and he wouldn't need it any more himself. It didn't matter so much what you gave on such occasions, it was just the idea of a gift.

When he reached George Square he found the horse from the livery stable with a boy at its head, standing outside Number 25, switching his tail at flies and now and then scraping his forefoot over the cobblestones. The saddlebags were in place. As he passed the drawing-room door on his way upstairs to get the farewell present Walter saw Mr. Mitchell standing with his back to the door bowing and bowing in an embarrassed sort of way. Anne came to the foot of the stairs and called in an insistent whisper,

"Wattie! Wattie! Mother wants you to come at once and say good-by to Mr. Mitchell——"

"I'm coming. I'm coming."

A silence had fallen when he entered the drawing-room, one of those restless silences that come when the farewells have all been said and for some reason the part-

ing is delayed. Walter marched up to the tutor with his
book in his hand.

"Mr. Mitchell, I have a parting present for you, to
be a memorandum of our friendship——" the book, very
limp and battered, fell open in his hands as he spoke
and showed margins decorated with pictures of animals
and scrawled over with notes that had nothing to do
with the lesson, "——of little value," continued Walter
earnestly, "but you know, Mr. Mitchell, that presents
are not to be estimated according to their intrinsic value
but according to the intention of the donor."

He was prepared to make his intention perfectly clear,
but it was not necessary. The good young man was immensely touched, and expressed himself as grateful both
for the intention and for the book itself, which he said
he would profit by rereading carefully.

"And there seems to be considerable reading-matter
in it besides that of the worthy Dr. Adam's authorship,"
remarked Mrs. Scott, cutting short his thanks. "Now we
must not keep you from your journey longer. Anne, the
packet of lunch for Mr. Mitchell. Please pay my respects
to your sister. You must be sure to let us know when you
come this way again, and we shall be glad to hear how
you get on in Arbroath . . ."

Bit by bit she got him down the steps and out to his
horse. He shook hands with them all again from the
saddle. In another minute he was gone.

"A very worthy young man," said Mrs. Scott. "Now,
Walter, come upstairs and we'll finish packing your
box."

As so many times before they went up the stairs together with their arms around each other, but now Walter's arm was over his mother's shoulder and his head, but for her cap, would have overtopped hers. He had grown.

14

KELSO

"SLINK over by me, Jamie, and I'll tell you a story."
Walter moved over on the form which, as the
visitor from Edinburgh and the only boy in the Kelso
school who studied Tacitus and Persius instead of the
Rudiments and Cornelius Nepos, he had all to himself
in the back of the room, and patted the bench beside him
invitingly. James Ballantyne, with a quick look toward
the front of the room where Lancelot Whale sat at his
desk behind a large book, slid hurriedly across the
aisle in a sitting-down posture and established himself
beside Wattie and behind Rob Waldie, who was wide
enough to shield him from view from the front.

"I haven't got my lesson yet," he whispered, "but no
matter. Go on."

"Did you ever hear of Canobie Dick, the horse-cooper
who fell in with Thomas the Rhymer on the west side
of the Eildon Hills one moonlight night?"

The breeze that came in through the open windows
blew over climbing roses on its way up from the Tweed.
Just beyond the window sill a water-wagtail tipped and

ran over the top of the stone wall, then stopped and flirted his long blade of a tail.

"Canobie Dick would have got the better of the devil himself on a horse-trade, but the stranger agreed without a murmur to the price he set and what's more he paid the money at once in bonnet pieces and gold unicorns and old coins like that."

Jamie's narrow sensitive face under his shock of dark hair was alive with interest, his dark eyes followed Walter's eagerly.

"The stranger invited Canobie Dick into his dwelling to drink half a mutchkin, but he gave him warning first, 'If you lose courage,' says he, 'at anything you see in there, you will rue it as long as you may live——' "

"Now, Walter Scott," the hoarse voice of Mr. Whale interrupted the tale, "peradventure you will be kind enough to take the beginners off my hands whilst I hear the others their Cornelius Nepos, and then we shall have time for our worthy Persius."

The room was full of the shuffling of feet as half of the lads took their places before the master and the rest, the little ones, gathered around Walter. He heard their rules and examples and set the industrious ones fresh tasks to do while he labored further with the slow ones, until at length Mr. Whale was free for a time and they could draw aside to do their reading together.

A strange creature Mr. Whale might be, with his huge, ungainly body, his checkered handkerchief, and his almost hysterical rage over puns made upon his name—a reference to Jonah or an odd fish put him beside himself—but he was an ardent classical scholar and far above, Walter thought, his present situation of ramming the mere foundations of Latin into the heads of sons of local tradesmen. That he thoroughly enjoyed his hours with Walter was almost pathetically evident. His large gaunt face lit up with pleasure, the movements of his awkward hands were quick and eager, he ejaculated with increasing frequency his favorite word of approbation, "Pro-di-gi-ous!"

On his side Walter enjoyed the hours too. He could go ahead with the sense of the Latin as fast as he liked, while Mr. Whale followed behind, so to speak, gathering up forms and endings for him.

After the day's stint of reading Walter recited a part of the speech of Galgacus which he was learning for the Public Examination next month, and then he was free for the day.

He came out into the Knowes, uncertain just which way he wished to turn. Directly across the common ground was Aunt Jenny's cottage, set on the edge of its big garden which went down to the Tweed. He thought of seeking the kitchen and asking Tibbie for something to eat; if she was in a good humor she would give it to him, but if she was not she would probably nab him and make him get ready now to go out for dinner with Aunt Jenny, and it was too early for that. To his left was the parish church in its churchyard under old trees. And behind him was the ruined Abbey. He would just have time to climb the tower. He swung around.

Not much was left of the ancient abbey of Kelso, once the richest if not the greatest of the four border abbeys, except the ruined West tower, the walls of the transepts, and a bit of the choir. Grass grew now under open sky where once monks paced in stained-glass dimness; harebells swayed in chinks of the stonework. In a corner of the tower the circular stone steps still remained. Carefully he climbed round and round, up and up, now half in darkness, now with the sunlight streaming through open places and making him screw up his eyes.

When the steps stopped he came out on a narrow ledge high up in the air. Here, no doubt, monks once came to look out anxiously over the countryside to see if the English were coming. You could see everything from here: Tweed, tucking the town of Kelso into the crook of his elbow, and Teviot slipping past Roxburgh Castle to meet Tweed in front of the great modern mansion of Fleurs. You could see Smailholm Tower and the Eildon Hills, once a single mountain which the wizard Michael Scott had cleft into three peaks with a single blow of his wand, and in the other direction the Cheviots blue in the distance, patterned with cloud shadows.

You could look down on Kelso and see the Market Place, and the Waldies' house on Bridge Street, where he and Aunt Jenny were going for dinner. You could see Captain Marjoribanks in his red coat and shining black boots, his sword at his side, coming across the bridge. Probably he was on his way to call on his Gloriana, to whom he wrote verses that had been collected into a slim volume called *Trifles in Verse of a Young Soldier.*

Very good verses they were, too. Rather like Horace. You could see Andrew Gemmels, the licensed beggar, striding along in his blue gown with the wind ruffling his white hair and long white beard.

He saw the schoolboys streaming down the street and picked a bit of mortar out of the wall to toss down on them. He had best be getting down himself now, or Aunt Jenny would be sending a searching party out for him.

He lingered for a last look, imagining the Abbey as it must have been in 1545 when the Earl of Hertford's army bore down on it. He thought of the twelve monks and ninety townsmen fighting desperately to save it from the invaders. When it was all over, the Abbey lay smoking in ruins, a line of wagons containing its treasures went winding away over the hills, its valiant defenders slept where they had fallen among its broken stones.

Very peaceful and happy the countryside looked now, but it had known *that*. Tweed had run red, and there had been bloodstains, probably, on the very stone he had his hand on now. You could not feel reverence enough when you thought of all that had been. You could only feel that somehow you had lived it yourself too, all the terror and the courage, the glory and the defeat.

"Wattie! Walter Scott! You, there, laddie, have you seen Walter Scott?"

It was as he had thought, Tibbie was sent out to look for him. He leaned over the parapet. "I'll be down directly."

Chuckling at the sight of her startled face upturned to

the sky, he scrambled down as fast as he could. Aunt Jenny was waiting in the parlor, bonneted, shawled, and gloved.

"You've time enough to make yourself neat," she said calmly. "I knew well you would be mooning somewhere among the ruins and so I sent Tibbie out for you in plenty of time. There will be no need for you to skimp on the brushing of your clothes."

No longer young, Miss Janet Scott was still beautiful, not only to those who loved her, like Cousin Barbara and himself and, he suspected, Mr. George Constable, but also to those who stood in some awe of her tongue, which could be sharp. She had what was considered an elegant figure, and very fine dark eyes and beautiful white teeth. Walter felt proud of her when they set forth together. There was nobody in Kelso who could compare with her in looks or intellect, and she would have held her own in Edinburgh.

The Waldies were Quakers. Rob's mother was known in Kelso as Lady Waldie, but she wore the gray garb of the Quakers and she spoke in the gentle Quaker way with thees and thous. They lived in a gray stone house on Bridge Street which, like almost all Kelso houses, had a garden bordering on the river. Wattie liked Rob Waldie well enough, though he had not the interest in tales and old things that Jamie Ballantyne had—but he had lost his heart to Lady Waldie.

"I've Quakers in my ancestry too," he told her at dinner.

"Hast thou? And how is that?"

"On both sides. There was a Walter Scott who turned Quaker in sixteen-something. His brother Sir William had him shut up for it in the Tolbooth in Edinburgh first, and then in Jedburgh jail, and had his children taken away from him."

"Sixteen-something. That must have been after George Fox came into the south of Scotland. He said afterwards that as he first set his horse's feet upon Scottish ground he felt the seed of grace to sparkle about him like innumerable sparks of fire."

"I suspect it was no the seeds of grace that sparkled in Walter Scott's brother William," observed Aunt Janet. "He got the court to decree him ten thousand pounds a year from his brother's property in order to bring up the children out of the faith their father was suffering for—and a fine profit he must have made out of that. Thus Quakerism died out of the Scott family. What Quaker blood have ye got on the other side, Wattie?"

"Mother's great-grandfather, Judge Swinton, was imprisoned in Edinburgh Castle itself."

The third guest at the table was Miss Goldie, the maiden lady who figured in Captain Marjoribanks's verses as Gloriana. She folded her lips tightly and crossed her hands, which were swathed in scarlet mitts, across her lean bosom. "I understand," she said archly, "that the Quakers do not hold with war."

Amusement glinted in Miss Jenny's fine eyes. "I doubt they would do away even with smart young recruiting officers, would they no, Lady Waldie?"

Miss Goldie pretended not to understand what Miss

Jenny meant, but she had to lower her eyes to hide her pleasure.

How in the world, wondered Wattie, did Miss Goldie ever look like a Gloriana to Captain Marjoribanks? Her hands in those red mitts were like two boiled lobsters.

"I'm afraid Wattie could never be a Quaker," went on Miss Jennie. "His head is ringing with the clash of swords and ancient battlecries till he can hardly hear a modern peaceable person speak."

"When wars are far enough in the past, we think only of the courage that went into them, not of the suffering and death," replied Lady Waldie.

"Plenty of cock-a-hoop courage is what Wattie likes, is it no, lad?"

The sweet was fresh strawberry tart with cream so thick that it had to be assisted from the pitcher with a spoon. Walter helped himself with such polite restraint that Lady Waldie took it away from him and served him as she thought it ought to be done.

"Thou needst plenty of cream and milk if thou'rt to gain flesh and be strong."

"Yes, is he no a gangling lad?" Miss Jenny spoke briskly, but her eyes were tender. "I've been wishing to have the young artist who is stopping with the minister make a portrait of Wattie for me, but I am waiting till he gets a bit stouter and ruddier. I have no wish to send him down to posterity as a whey-faced sprig!"

"He does very fine likenesses, they tell me."

A portrait? *Well,* thought Wattie.

Dinner over, Lady Waldie led him into the library

where books lined the walls on three sides and on the fourth the Tweed tore past the window. What a place to read that window seat would be!

"Rob tells me thou'rt fond of reading. Hast thou books enough?"

"We-ell, I get some from the circulating library——"

"Dear me. Ancient trash, most of it. Come here whenever thou'dst like books. Thou'rt welcome to all thou canst read."

"May I take one with me today?"

"Most assuredly."

His eager hand fell first on a little brown volume near the fireplace. He opened it. *Reliques of Ancient Englishe Poetry*, the title ran, *Consisting of Old, Heroic Ballads*——

"Here's the one for me!"

"Which is it? Bishop Percy's *Reliques?* There are three volumes to that; better take them all, they are so small."

He had them under his arm when they left late in the afternoon. He had also a book on the Society of Friends which Lady Waldie gave him with a smile.

"I ask thee to take it with thee," she explained, "but I do not require thee to promise to read it. I should not like to feel responsible for a broken promise. But take it anyhow, and then I shall know that I have at least exposed thee to it!"

15

UNDER THE PLANE TREE

WITH his books under his arm Walter stopped the next morning in the kitchen for some of the fresh oatcakes that were sending a warm and nutty fragrance all through the house. He found Tibbie Hunter pausing in her work to talk to old Andrew Gemmels, who lounged in the chimney corner with his gray eyes cast heavenward and a satirical smile playing around the corner of his mouth. His commanding profile, tilted at the most effective angle, his white hair and long white beard, his light-blue gown, made a picture against the smoky gray stone—as he very well knew. Walter had often heard Miss Jenny comment dryly on Andrew's graceful poses.

"Ye should settle doon," Tibbie was haranguing him. "Here ye are, ninety-five years of age, traipsing over the countryside with your staff and bowl, when ye ken weel ye've eneuch siller quilted up in that blue gown of yours to pay for a neat little cottage somewhere——"

"And what wad I do in a neat little cottage, seeing the same walls and floor and hearthstanes day after day and week after week? And what wad the countryside do without Andrew Gemmels, the best-known gaberlunzie on both sides of the Border, that brings news and——"

"Ye micht sit and rest and think prayerfully o' your approaching end——"

"Bow, wow, wow, woman! Womenfolk are aye fashing theirsel's aboot what they hae nae business wi'."

"Andrew," said Walter, leaning over the table for another oatcake, "is it true that on the King's birthday you get a penny for every year of his age?"

"True as the blue sky, my dear. And every year on the King's birthday a new carle gets his blue gown and pewter badge. As many King's bedesmen as the King has years, that's the rule as ever was and ever will be."

"All you have to do is pray for the King's long life?"

"Aye, and a very congenial task it is too, especially as each year that His Majesty is spared to us is anither penny in the pooch."

"Is it true you were in the army once?"

"True as the blue sky."

Walter hesitated. Should he go on and read the book that was fairly crying out under his arm, or should he stay and talk to Andrew?

The gaberlunzie took out his gold watch, cocked one bushy eyebrow at it, and got up, rising till his white head all but brushed the dark oak beams of the ceiling. "I must awa' to Rob Murdoch's in the Horse Market. I gave him my word I wad help him mend his fiddle."

"You'll be back again?" said Walter. It was true that the ancient beggar carried a gold watch—he must tell Jamie Ballantyne.

Andrew took up the staff that was nearly as tall as

he was. "I couldna go aff to St. Boswell's before I have a game at the dambrod with Mistress Tibbie."

Tibbie tittered at the idea of her having any skill on the dambrod, but Walter understood old Andrew's words as a promise that there would be a time later for old songs and tales.

Now for Bishop Percy. He helped himself to more oatcakes and went out into the garden.

It lay between the house and the bright Tweed, splashed with sunshine and dim with shade, fragrant, overgrown, mysterious. He passed by the kitchen garden and the lawns and formal alleys and threaded his way through the little "labyrinth" toward the most secret and withdrawn place he knew.

The hedge-lined paths, half in shade, bent and turned this way and that. Here was a snail leaving a silver streak that glistened in a scarf of sunshine, there a bright flower had fought its way through from the bed on the other side of the hedge. Now the path split into two and he took the one on the left. In another moment he was at the "bower" in the very core of the maze.

The old rustic summerhouse was falling to pieces. It had lurched to a crazy angle and part of the roof was gone. Over it a huge oriental plane tree spread its thick branches like a tent. From above—from the upper windows of the house, for instance, or the pear tree by the kitchen door—you could not see the summerhouse at all. You saw just the hill of leaves that was the plane tree.

Inside, it was like a little, hidden, secret room. Thin wisps of sunshine sifted through the chinks in the leaves;

the air was green and cool and smelled of old wood and bark and the sun on the garden round about. You heard nothing but the rustle of a leaf, the buzz of a bee that came blundering through, or now and then the song of a chaffinch in the hedge or the cries of sea-birds swooping over the Tweed.

Walter settled himself comfortably on the firmest part of the bench, put his feet up on the railing, and opened the first volume of Percy's *Reliques*.

There was an essay at the beginning that he meant to skip but a few words caught his eye and he read on, amazed. Ballads, the sort of tale Aunt Jenny used to sing and Mrs. Irving recite to him at tea time, that he had always loved but thought a kind of homely country thing—why, this man was writing about them seriously, as if he considered them worthy of being studied and explained. He read on a bit farther, and then decided to come back to that later. The "Ballad of Otterbourne," a few pages over, was beckoning irresistibly.

> It fell about the Lammastide
> When the muirmen win their hay——

It was near Lammastide now. Probably on just such a day as this, four hundred years ago, Earl Douglas rode into Northumberland with the Gordons and the Graemes and the Lindsays at his back and were surprised during the night by Lord Percy at Otterbourne.

> But up then spake a little page
> Before the peep of dawn,

"Oh waken ye, waken ye, my good lord,
  For Percy's hard at hand."

Walter liked that little page. He *was* the lad, waking
in the clear moonlight and seeing the enemy approach,
rousing his lord, listening with a chill in the very mar-
row of his bones when the great Douglas said:

"But I have dreamed a dreary dream,
  Beyond the Isle of Skye,
I saw a dead man win a fight,
  And I think that man was I."

Perhaps, though the ballad did not say so, he ran after
his lord with the helmet that he forgot when he belted
on his broadsword and ran to the field. But it was too
late. The Douglas had fallen, wounded in the head.

Then he called on his little foot-page,
  And said, "Run speedilie
And get my ain dear sister's son,
  Sir Hugh Montgomerie."

And now Wattie stopped being the page and was Sir
Hugh Montgomery instead, a young knight, strong and
valiant, burying the Douglas by the bracken bush "with
the saut tear in his ee," turning resolute to face the Percy
and swakking swords till the blood ran down between.

"Now yield ye, yield ye, Percy," he said,
  "Or else I vow I'll lay thee low——"

Percy naturally refused to yield, until he learned that
it was the Montgomery whom he fought. Then he struck

his sword's point in the ground. Sir Hugh, "a courteous knight," quickly took him "by the honde."

> This deed was done at Otterbourne
> About the breaking of the day;
> Earl Douglas was buried at the bracken bush
> And the Percy led captive away.

What days those were! Brave and honorable men on both sides—and lads his own age or less serving as foot-pages to the heroes!

He read "Fair Rosamond" next because the word "maze" leapt out of the page at him. The King had built Rosamond a bower at Woodstock in the center of a maze of which only he knew the secret; but the jealous queen made her way in by a clue of a "thridde of silke," and poisoned her.

He read the "Gaberlunzie Man" because of Andrew Gemmels, and laughed out loud. He read "Sir Patrick Spens" and "Edward, Edward."

The world around him melted away. There was just the hidden green place in which he sat, and the volumes that he was devouring in great gulps.

Here was his old friend Hardyknute. It was not an old ballad at all. It was a modern imitation and by a lady at that, a Mrs. Wardlaw, whose maiden name was Halket, aunt to the late Sir Peter Halket of Pitferran, who pretended that she had found it on some scraps of old paper. He read it all through, though he knew it by heart, just for the pleasure of seeing the familiar words in print.

"Sir Andrew Barton." This was new to him. "He is a proud Scot that robbs on the seas." This one was going to be good.

> "Fight on, my men," Sir Andrew sayes,
>   "A little Ime hurt but yett not slane;
> Ile but lye down and bleede a while
> And then Ile rise and fight againe.

> "Fight on, my men," Sir Andrew sayes,
>   "And never flinche before the foe;
> And stand fast by Saint Andrew's cross
> Until you hear my whistle blow."

They never heard his whistle blow. He was dead. The English had killed him. But even the English were sorry that they had killed such a foe.

> "I wold give," quoth the king, "a thousand merkes
>   This man were alive as hee is dead."

He read that one twice.

Now and then he shifted his position to ease his leg. Once he moved so that the changing light would fall better on his book. Once he had a vague notion that time was passing, but he forgot it when he turned the page. "Robin Hood and Guy of Gisborne."

"*Walter Scott!*" The plump red face of his Cousin Barbara peered through the leaves at him. She turned her head and called over her shoulder, "I've found him, Jenny! Oh, she's gone. Tibbie! Tibb*ee!* Tell Miss Scott I've found him."

Walter reluctantly closed his book over his finger. Well, they had found him. Probably they wanted him to run an errand.

"I'm here," he said resignedly. "Did Aunt Jenny want me?"

"Have ye been here all day?"

"All day?"

"Yes, all day. Oh, Wattie, you look so vague if I didna know different I'd think ye were light in the upper story. The denner hour's come and gone long ago. We've been a'most mad with worry—we were ready to think you'd fallen in the river."

He looked about him. The fingers of sunshine came over his left shoulder now instead of his right one. The air had the fragrance of afternoon, of grass and blossoms warmed all day by the sun. He got up from his wooden seat and found to his surprise that he was stiff and sore.

" 'She sought him east, she sought him west,' " he quoted tragically:

"She sought him braid and narrow,
    Syne in the clifting of a craig,
        She found him drowned in Yarrow."

"It's ill jesting about such things, Walter. Reading all day and forgetting your dinner. Tuts. I've never seen such a lad."

Facts and dates might fall away from Walter's mind like snowflakes in a thaw, but anything that interested him stuck fast without any effort at all. From that day forth his head was full of ballads and his conversation was made up of excerpts from them. He had a quotation for every occasion. If his aunt wished him to take a note to Lady Waldie inviting her to tea, he went off declaiming:

"Where sall I get a bonny boy
    That will win hose and shoon,
    That will gae to Lord Barnard's ha'
    And bid his lady come?"

When Tibbie Hunter grumbled over her work and complained of being too old and tired for this eternal scrubbing and polishing, he consoled her with:

"Stately stept he east the ha'
    And stately stept he west,
    Full seventy years he now had seen
    Wi' scarce seven years of rest."

He went to school proclaiming lines from the "Gaberlunzie Man":

" 'Oh wow,' quo' he, 'were I as free
    As first when I saw this countrie
    How blythe and merry wad I bee!' "

When Aunt Jenny tried to shoo him off to sit for the portrait the visiting artist was painting of him, he would hold an imaginary picture out at arm's length and say with a puzzled expression:

"Is this my father Philip?
    Or is't my brother John?
    Or is't my true love Willie
    From Scotland new come home?"

And when at length his family and friends turned on him in exasperation and declared that they had had enough ballads and would be grateful for some plain everyday English for a change, he said cheerfully:

> "I heare a bird sing in myne eare
>   That I must either fight or flee"

and off he went to roam alone along the Tweed roaring "Sir Andrew Barton" to the sea gulls and cormorants.

The days slipped past. Raspberries followed the strawberries, and gooseberries, hairy and translucently green, the raspberries. The corn ripened in the fields and was cut and stacked. Dark-bibbed peewits roamed among the stubble, and poppies that were small enough to escape the scythe made scarlet blobs in the shorn golden fields. The heather came to the hills. Clouds heavy with rain gathered in piles in the sky and sudden showers pitted the swift brown Tweed or blotted out parts of the distant hills.

After the Public Examination had taken place (at which Walter spouted the speech of Galgacus with a zest which his audience understood better than the Latin) and school was over till October, he and Jamie Ballantyne and Dustiefoot the Cairn terrier went off together every day on long jaunts. Sometimes they walked, and sometimes, when they were going farther afield, they rode on ponies. They went to Sandyknowe to look at the old farm and prowl around Smailholm Tower, to Kirk Yetholm to see the gypsy settlement, to Melrose and Dryburgh for the ruined abbeys. They would start before

breakfast and somewhere along the way they would find
the ideal spot to eat their bread and cheese and cold
beef——

"'Snug in a glen where nane could see,'" Walter
would chant:

"The twa wi' kindlie sport and glee
    Cut frae new cheese a whang——"

and then they would explore until almost dinner time.
Jamie was not the companion that Irving and Adam
were, but he was a comfortable sort of lad in his quiet
way, and he would listen forever to Wattie's stories.

In the late afternoons Walter and his aunt loved to
walk together along the river. Corn crakes called in the
bushes; herons stood long-legged among the reeds on
the opposite bank or, heaving themselves up on slowly
flapping wings, flew away at their approach. Men, waist-
deep in the rushing water, fished for salmon, and in the
meadows rabbits gathered in tribes.

The last day before Walter was to go back to Edinburgh they crossed the bridge and walked along the
Teviot to Roxburgh Castle to make it a farewell visit.
The sun had come out after rain and every blade of grass
and every leaf glistened. Shadows fell over the old castle,
softening its scars; brown and golden wallflowers grew
close to the gray stone wall.

"Have you ever noticed how wallflowers around old
ruins always smell sweeter at nightfall?" said Aunt
Jenny. "Can you remember those that used to grow
around Smailholm Tower when you were a bairn?"

They sat down on a crumbling bit of stone wall. Walter thought back.

"Yes, of course I do. Sandy Ormiston used to carry me up there and I'd scramble about in the grass until Tibbie came up to fetch me. I remember there was honeysuckle there too, and Sandy used to tell me stories. I thought the tower was enormous. And it isn't at all. When I saw it the other day it was quite small."

"Sandy used to blow twice on his whistle when he wanted Tibbie to come for you." She turned to look at him thoughtfully as if she were seeing into his mind. "Can you remember the thunderstorm?"

When he shook his head she went on, "A terrific thunderstorm came up one day and we couldn't find you. Nobody had any idea where you were. We ran about distractedly, until I remembered the tower and rushed up there thinking you would be struck or drowned or at any rate terrified. But there you were, with the lightning flashing all round you, clapping your hands and shouting, 'Bonny! Bonny! Dae't again! Dae't again!' "

Walter listened with the reverent attention that one gives to accounts of one's infant exploits. Miss Jenny flicked the end of his nose gently with her forefinger and said, teasing him, "Remarkable bairn you were, Wattie. Prodigious, as our friend Mr. Whale would say."

She rose and brushed off a leaf that had drifted down into the lap of her dress. "We had better be going back now."

He turned for a last look at the castle. The shadows

were deepening around its feet, but the sun lay golden on its empty towers. He had again that feeling that had come to him one day on the top of the abbey and once more when he was reading ballads under the plane tree in the garden, a sense of the heart-tearing beauty and bravery of the olden times, the impact of their reality. He was the knight riding forth with a plume in his helmet and his sword hanging from his belt; he was the lady watching from the window of her bower as long as her lord was in sight; he was the little page boy who saw his master's horse returning with the empty saddle. And he was Walter Scott, seeing what they saw and feeling what they felt so keenly that his ribs fairly pinched his swelling heart.

16

ELECTRICITY

W ALTER was tired of hearing about this Dr. James Graham. He wished people would find something else to talk about. All Edinburgh was full of him, his Temple of Health, his Medical, Moral, and Religious lectures in St. Andrew's Chapel (admission three shillings) his miraculous cures, his good looks, his magnificent electrical apparatus. It was bad enough to hear the well-worn phrases every time you skirted the edge of a grown-up conversation, but when even the lads at college began on him it was too much.

"I think he might do your leg good, Wattie," said Irving in the middle of the class in the Humanities. "Why don't you go to him?"

Nobody thought of paying attention to work in the mild and good-natured Mr. Hill's class. It was a riot from the moment it began until the students noisily clattered out. Walter and Irving and Adam sat on a form together and cheerfully discussed life, literature, and medicine while they forgot most of the Latin that they had learned in the High School.

"Father thinks he has the right ideas about a vege-

table diet," contributed Adam, "but he thinks his no-
tions as to temperature are uncivilized, sir, uncivilized.
No feather beds and no blankets, windows open wide all
night, and a cold bath morning and night to warm
you up."

Walter chuckled, picturing the good Dr. Ferguson's
reaction to such a regime. He was famous for his fur-
lined coat, worn indoors and out, and for his preoccu-
pation with the temperature. He consulted the thermometer in his parlor every few minutes and if the
mercury fell so much as a degree he had the whole household in a dither.

"I think I'll stay away from Dr. Graham in the winter,"
said Walter perfunctorily.

As a matter of fact he was going to see Dr. Graham as
soon as Robert's outfit was ready and he was got off to
his new career, but he did not want to talk about it be-
forehand or even think about it. There was no use getting your hopes up too high.

His mother and father had come home from the doctor's lecture in Carrubber's Close afire with the thought
of this amazing new electrical treatment. Nobody knew
much about electricity except that it had mysterious and
vast potentialities, but it stood to reason, they argued,
that if you take a leg that is stiff and numb, or even stiff
and aching, and impregnate it through and through with
electricity, it ought to become nimble. This man had
done more wonderful things than that, if you could believe the reports that came from New England, where

he had first won fame, and, what was very much more important, from London itself.

To walk instead of limping. To run. To start even with everybody else. What it would mean!

Better not even think about it till it happened.

"It will take Robert six months to get to Bombay," he said.

"Why would anybody want to give up the navy for the East India Company?" said Adam.

The master gave out an order from his desk and they all turned the pages of their books rapidly with a fluttering noise that sounded all over the room in a parody of diligence.

"There's no advancement in the navy in peace times."

"My cousin James Clerk is going into the navy." Irving groped under the desk for his book, which had slipped to the floor. "He's Will's brother. You don't know Will, do you?"

"No," said Walter, and made a bet of a lump of jube with Adam that Irving would mention the fact that his uncle, Sir John Clerk, had discovered the tactics which Rodney used in his great battle. But Irving said only,

"You'd like Will."

The class dragged on in idleness and mirth unchecked. Somebody dropped a marble and it rolled resoundingly over the wooden floor toward the lowest corner where the beams had settled. All the feet shuffled at once in response to the signal, dust rose in clouds, the very walls shook, and Mr. Hill shouted ineffectually.

Walter yawned. They had done it so often that there was no fun in it any more, just boredom and disgust.

They really ought to be careful how they stamped in this old building—they'd shake it down some day. People were always talking about new buildings for the college and writing letters to the *Evening Courant* about it, but nothing ever was done. Classes went on in these old, crow-stepped, gable-ended buildings, dilapidated inside and out, with the dust of years in all the cracks and the musty smell of the centuries in every stone. This very room they were in belonged to the house that had been partly blown up with gunpowder when Darnley was killed. Probably Mary Stuart had trodden these floors when she came that last time to see him.

Dr. Graham. Dr. James Graham. "How to Build the Human Body into a Fair and Firm Temple of Health." Electrical apparatus and mud baths. And if it should do what they hoped!

Walter paid his first visit to Dr. Graham on a raw sleety day early in December. Whenever he thought of that day afterwards he remembered how the sleet had stung his face. He remembered, too, Lord Monboddo shuddering home from the Court through the storm with his own scanty gray locks being whipped across his face while beside him, safe and dry in a sedan chair, rode his large, elegant, curled-and-powdered wig. Ride himself the old judge would not, be the weather what it might. But most of all he remembered the suspended clammy state of his inward feelings, half hope, half premonition of disappointment.

He found Dr. Graham's house, three doors from the High Street on the new South Bridge. He went in. The door opened into a hallway, in which a large statue of the Venus de' Medici glimmered palely in the dimness and took up so much room that you had to turn sidewise to squeeze past her. Off the hall was the doctor's office.

He was early. The old Earl of Hopetoun without his wig or coat sat nervously in a large armchair hung around with a collar and a belt of magnets, looking like nothing so much as an Indian chief in his best war jewelry. About him hovered the celebrated Dr. Graham, very tall and handsome in a white-and-silver suit with black silk stockings on his shapely legs, uttering scientific phrases about the magnetic field in clipped English speech. He turned his head for a moment as Walter came in, and Walter, sitting down deprecatingly on the edge of a chair near the door, felt the doctor's quick glance at his leg, and flushed.

"I think this will be all for today, my lord."

An assistant, a mawkish young man with a pimply face, helped to remove the magnets and to restore to the Earl his coat and wig.

"I advise strongly, Lord Hopetoun, nothing for dinner but kail and onions, tea, bread in moderation, no animal fats." He smiled, and Walter, watching, felt the sudden charm of that smile. "All flesh is grass, you know. And let me see you again at the same time next week—if that is convenient to you, of course."

Walter's turn came.

"This is the lad Dr. Rutherford spoke to me about.

Yes, yes. How are you, my boy? That is good, that is good, but we want to make you even better. Now let us see. Arthur, you may help here."

Walter submitted to the examination, thankful that at least he had been able to persuade his mother to let him come alone. The doctor's hands were firm and light and sure; his handsome face was grave and absorbed; confidence and sympathy were in his voice. He had Walter stand, walk, climb up and down steps improvised out of a footstool, a chair, and a table.

"Yes. Yes. I see."

Sleet hissed against the window. Out in the street a Highland chairman swore shrilly in Gaelic.

"Bad boys tickle the chairmen's legs with a pin at the end of a stick when they are carrying a load," said Dr. Graham, smiling. Walter smiled too, but he was amused by Dr. Graham's English accent—it was so quick and so brittle. An English boy had come to Mr. Fraser's class in the High School once and the whole school had laughed itself sore over his voice.

The assistant Arthur with an important air began to drag forward a table with an elaborate arrangement of cylinders and disks and wires upon it. The doctor motioned for Walter to sit in the chair in front of it.

"Will I get the magnets?" said Walter.

Dr. Graham was too busy with his apparatus to answer for a moment, then he said:

"Electricity is a fluid flowing in a greater or less degree through all bodies. Some bodies are said to be vitreously charged, some resinously. We suit the treatment to the charge that is present in the body. I believe this to be better suited to your case."

Walter watched every motion with interest, came nearer when he was told to, stretched forth his hand and grasped the lever that was pointed out to him. A shock went shooting up his arm and across his chest, a strange sensation, not exactly unpleasant, but very odd.

"Hold it longer this time."

His fingers quivered and stuck together; the weird thrill went up his arm in waves.

"It—it's my leg that's lame," he ventured.

"Yes, yes, I understand. Electricity is a fluid flowing all through the body; if we establish contact with it anywhere it reaches all parts."

That sounded all right. The doctor spoke further of von Kleist at Kummin, and Muschenbrock at Leyden, of Dr. Franklin of Philadelphia, and William Watson's important experiments in London. Presently the treatment was over.

Walter went home with his nerves on edge, feeling unaccountably low in spirits. He liked the doctor fine, he answered their questions at home with an impatience quite unlike his usual good-natured way; the doctor seemed to know a great deal about electricity; he had said Wattie was resinously charged. Yes, he . . .

His father went with him for the next treatment and had a long talk with the doctor. The lawyer tentatively produced a few electrical phrases which the doctor received as if in a desert of human waste he had met at last one intelligent man.

There was another treatment, and another. Between them Walter saw his Uncle Daniel Rutherford. He felt all their loving, troubled eyes upon him, watching to see if he was limping any the less. Dr. Graham suggested a mud bath, and Walter had that too. But only one mud bath. He objected to it so strenuously that it was not repeated, and soon his visits to Dr. Graham were discontinued altogether.

Nobody knew just when hope, which had never been very robust at best, flickered out. It was conceded that electricity was still in its infancy, that in some instances Dr. Graham's apparatus did indeed do all that was claimed for it, that his ideas about diet and fresh air and cold baths were applicable to some cases—usually other than the speaker's. Even before he returned to London, Edinburgh had stopped talking about him.

Mrs. Scott's disappointment went deepest and lasted longest. Walter had quickly cast his own aside. Everything had been tried now, he thought, newly flayed sheepskins, the waters of Bath, sea-bathing at Prestonpans, and electricity, and he might as well settle down to being a lamiter. After all, he could go wherever anybody else went—a little more slowly perhaps—and the other lads paid little attention to it now.

Though he remained as lame as he had ever been, his general health definitely improved as the winter wore on. His mother could draw comfort from that. So much at least had electricity and mud done for him.

"Look to a gown of gold," his father quoted, "and you will at least get a sleeve of it."

17

THE GREEK BLOCKHEAD

THAT's what I call a vile view from nature," said Walter, and threw down his brush. Nothing was going right today. First the Greek, and now this.

The anxious little Prussian Jew who was giving him lessons in painting answered soothingly.

"Now, Mr. Valter, dot iss not vile. It is chust dot you go too fast. You do not stop to consider, to look mit your eyes half shut, so, to analyze—mass—color—composition. You rush at it. You begin at vun side of de canvas and you pent across as if you were writink a letter. Iss dot any vay to do?"

Walter picked up his brush again. "Let me do a castle. I'm good at them."

"No, now pleass. You are goot at castles because you put in effery stone in the turret exactly so, but iss dot vy your mother sends you to me, to learn to pent castles like a child buildink block houses? Now, ve vill scrape it all off, and you vill start again and pent the view from dis vindow."

Walter went to the window and looked out. The drawing-master's room was in the attic of an old land in St. John Street, a dingy little room indeed, but it had a magnificent view of Edinburgh and the Pentland Hills. It was a spring day set down in February. Roofs glistened black and wet in the sunshine, and clouds made purple splotches on the brown hills. But how could you paint it? There was nothing to take hold of.

He would like to have a handsome oil painting to take home to his mother to hang in her dressing-room. She could see that if he couldn't learn Greek, at least he could paint.

Mr. Burrill, whose pudgy hands were quick and sure as Walter's long-fingered, slender ones could never be, was making light marks on the canvas. His black eyes, close together on either side of his mountainous nose, were eager.

"Now, see, Mr. Valter. Put your hills here, and your mass of houses *here,* to balance, and haf the light comink down slant-vise, so, and dun't try to draw in effery chimney pot."

Almost everybody else in Mr. Dalzell's first Greek class had a smattering of the language when they began, but Walter had not even known the alphabet. He wasn't certain of it now. There was no pleasure in being in a class where nearly everybody was better than he was. He didn't like Greek anyhow. It was a very inferior language. And furthermore, Homer as a poet was very inferior to—well, to Ariosto.

By jing, this paper that he had to write for class! That's what he'd do. He'd compare Homer with Ariosto, to Homer's disadvantage. He'd pulverize Homer. Probably nobody else in the class knew anything much about Ariosto; they'd see that he was not so stupid as he seemed. It was a matter of taste, that was all. He would stop at Dr. Blacklock's on the way home and borrow *Orlando* again.

He felt suddenly cheerful. Standing off from his picture, he looked at it with his head on one side, then he limped forward and put a dab of purple on a roof, then backed off again and looked at it with his head on the other side, in a manner he believed to be professional.

"Tell me some more about your father," he said graciously to Mr. Burrill.

It was strange to think that a little smouch like this had a father who had been a spy in the armies of Frederick of Prussia. The stories he told showed life as a tremendous and thundering affair—and he himself was small, anxious, unsuccessful.

The thick voice went on, interrupting itself now and then to make some despairing suggestion about a color or a line. Walter was thinking of his essay on Homer versus Ariosto, the quotations he would use and the bits of odd information he could drag in.

"I myself," he heard Mr. Burrill say, "have seen vounded Hussars piled on a wagon in a retreat, vatching their own blood dripping down through the straw."

Walter looked up, startled. It was as if something bigger than either of them had come into the room.

St. Giles's bell rang out in the silence and was answered by the Tron.

"The hour's up," said Walter. He added a neat spiral

of smoke to a chimney before he thrust his brushes into the pot of turpentine.

He wrote his essay and turned it in with some satisfaction. Ten pages of foolscap, and his handwriting had become fine and small during the last year.

Dr. Dalzell—pronounced Dalyell—taught Greek. In his way he was as mild as Dr. Hill, but nobody thought of taking liberties with him, perhaps because of the formality in his slow, gentle voice, or because you had to be respectful before his whole-souled enthusiasm for his beloved classics. He had too a mild and innocent way of making very quotable remarks that would be repeated with chuckles all over Edinburgh. Nobody quite wanted to be the subject of "Dalzell's latest."

Walter, after he had handed in his composition, felt some qualms. But the professor, when he read it, was quite too angry to make a *bon mot* about it. He haled Walter before him.

"Dunce you are, sir," he said furiously, "and dunce you will remain." He glared at Walter in silence while some sort of struggle obviously went on within him. "But I'm blest," he said at last with the surprise he could not suppress, "if I can conceive where you acquired the quantity of out-of-the-way knowledge you display."

And that, thought Walter philosophically, was the nearest he would ever come to shining at Greek.

That evening Archibald MacGuffog came to see him. Surprised and taken aback by the visit—for as Archibald was the son of an innkeeper, an excellent Greek scholar, and sat in the front of the classroom, and Walter was the son of a Writer to the Signet, loathed Greek, and sat in the back of the room, they had barely exchanged two words before—he received his guest in the hall. Mrs. Cockburn and his mother were having tea in the parlor, and he did not feel like inviting Archibald upstairs to the room he and Tom shared.

Archibald seemed unconscious of the omission. He began to talk as soon as he was inside the door. The lamplight fell on his lean, dark, almost comically serious face with the short upper lip and big teeth, and threw the rest of his thin awkward body into shadow.

"I've come to talk to ye about the Greek," he said earnestly.

"Well, and what about it?"

"Did ye know ye had the name of the Greek Blockhead?"

"No, but I——"

"Yes, ye have, and it's a very great peety. There's no need for ye to have it. It's your own silliness. It's a pose you've adopted. You could be at the top of the class if ye pit yer mind to it. Man, it makes me fair sick to see anybody wasting opporchunities as you are. If ye don't get the Greek now ye'll never get it, and ye'll be sorry all your life. Nobody is really educated that hasna the Greek."

Walter was nettled. It was none of Archibald's business whether he had the Greek or not. What made him think he could intrude into Walter's house and deliver a lecture on the subject?

"I don't happen to like Greek. It's just a matter of taste."

"Do ye like being called the Greek Blockhead? If ye set to work now ye could redeem yoursel' and make everybody forget ye were ever called that. Here's what I've come to tell ye. If ye pit yer mind to the Greek, I'll help ye. I'll help ye every day after class and I'll help ye in the evenings. There's not another mind in the class any better than yours, if ye wad use it, and I'll pledge you my word, if ye'll let me help ye, I'll bring ye forward with the foremost in the class."

Walter wondered uneasily if they could hear this exhortation in the parlor. It was good of Archibald, of course. Probably what he said was true, too; probably he could drag Walter to the top of the class, or near it. He was a fine Greek scholar, there was no doubt about that, and his respect for the language was almost as vast as Dr. Dalzell's own. But just the same, Walter had no desire to spend his afternoons and evenings being coached by Archibald MacGuffog. The Greek Blockhead? Pooh. It was all over the college that young Walter Scott had read *Orlando Furioso* and considered Ariosto a greater poet than Homer.

"It's very kind of you, but I couldn't accept it." He tried to be civil, but his voice sounded only sulky, even to himself. "I've no head for Greek. Likely you'd be disappointed."

"Ye mean ye won't try."

The poor lad looked crestfallen. There was no anger in his thin face, only sorrow.

"Ye'll regret it all your life," he repeated, fumbling with the door knob, "not having the Greek."

Walter's conscience stirred, but ineffectually. He watched Archibald go.

They never met again. A few times Walter saw Archibald from a distance, but not to speak to. The next October he did not appear in Professor Dalzell's second Greek class, and they learned that he had died in the summer.

Nobody understood why Walter Scott took Archibald MacGuffog's death so much to heart.

"It is a tragedy, of course," Mrs. Scott said, "a brilliant young mind—but he wasn't a friend of yours, Wattie, was he?"

"Not exactly." He could not tell her of that offer of help rejected in the lamplight. "It's just that life is so—so . . ." *Queer* was what he meant, but it was not just the word for it either.

"Yes, it *is,* isn't it," agreed his mother.

They sat on in companionable silence for a while without lighting the candles, though it was dark now.

That autumn he wrote an essay for Professor John Bruce's class in Ethics which Professor Bruce selected to be read before Principal Robertson. It was considered an honor, but somehow it had no meaning for Walter. Just a couple of professors giving a good lad a pat on the head. It wasn't life.

18

A BLOW IN THE DARK

IT happened without an instant's warning, when he and Tom were skirmishing in their bedroom. Tom had a poem that Walter had written and was reading it out in a loud, jeering voice, and Walter was for taking it forcibly away from him. They wrestled foot to foot, laughing, panting, Walter's long arm slowly overhauling Tom's shorter one.

"Ye limmer, would ye trifle with Willie wi' the Bolt Foot?"

But it was not his lame leg that caused the trouble. A blood vessel that he never even suspected that he had, broke within him. There was a stab of pain, quick and sharp like the prick of a knife. And then catastrophe.

"Let go a minute—I feel—Tom, don't——"

"Aha, Poet William Boltfoot, I have thee by the short hairs— Wattie, what's wrong wi' ye?"

His ears rang; hot black mists rose about him, pressing against his face, covering his eyes. He heard Tom's frightened gasp, "I'll fetch Mother," and then nothing more.

The next thing he knew they were lifting him on

to the bed, James Wilkinson and Tom between them, and his mother, white-faced, held his limp hand, feeling with unsteady fingers for his pulse.

"Stay very still, my lamb," she said when she saw his eyes open. "Lie still and dinna try to talk. I've sent a caddie for your Uncle Daniel."

He closed his eyes and then opened them again hastily; when his eyes were shut he felt as if he were falling and whirling through darkness.

A caddie, running through the wet streets to fetch Uncle Daniel. If the doctor were not at home, he would know where to find him. Caddies knew everybody and where they were likely to be at any time. He wanted to say, "Was't Green-Breeks you sent after Uncle Daniel?" but his lips were stiff and his voice suddenly difficult. It didn't want to start and then it didn't want to stop. "Green-Breeks?" he managed. The words went floating around the room like a little black cloud; part of him went floating with it and part of him trailed behind on the bed.

His mother leaned over to catch the words. "I didna get what you said, but don't try to talk, Wattie. He'll be here soon."

Tom understood. "No, not Green-Breeks. Donald Purdie."

Green-Breeks was a caddie now. Green-Breeks had been hurt once. Something about the banner Lady Elizabeth gave them. Lady Elizabeth would be married soon. To an Englishman. A great come-down. She should never have gone to London.

Tom looked frightened. He's frightened about me, thought Walter with a flash of clarity, and well he may be. I feel so ill. I feel so terribly—ill. Oh dear . . . Oh dear. . . . The hot mist closed around him again.

Dr. Daniel Rutherford came, looked serious, and bled him. The ways of doctors were past understanding. You had a hemorrhage, and then they bled you some more. It wasn't sensible, thought Walter, but then he was not a physician.

Uncle Daniel and James got him into bed. He was weak, so weak that he could not raise his arm to put it into the sleeve of his nightgown, but his head was clear again. He felt a kind of surprise and bafflement at this calamity that had come upon him, as if he had been set upon from ambush by an unseen enemy and overthrown. His lameness he knew and understood, but what was this?

Mr. Alexander Wood, the surgeon, was called in for consultation. Kind old Sandy Wood. When Walter was at the High School he used to see him come out of the Infirmary with his cocked hat over one eye, his walking stick over his shoulder, his dog at his heels, and set out briskly for his home in York Place. He had a pet sheep named Willy that was pastured in the empty lot by the excise office. Willy used to come up to the fence and stick his head into Mr. Wood's pocket for the goodies that were always there for him.

Walter looked up into the long-chinned, shrewd, kindly face bending over him and attempted a smile. "How's Willy?" Again the words that flashed so nimbly through his mind came forth slowly and heavily, like clumsy scows moored to a wharf.

"You must not talk, Walter," his uncle cut him off.

Dr. Graham drew up a chair, took Walter's wrist in one hand and balanced his fat gold repeater in the other.

"Willy is full of the deil as ever," he said, "and I have a raven now. The old carline in the ale and porter shop in North Castle Street keeps him for me. He sits on a perch in the window and watches for my coming."

Mrs. Scott hovered anxiously at the foot of the bed while the doctors made their examination. Presently they all went out of the room. As the door was closing after them Walter heard old Sandy Wood say, "I would recommend blistering rather than bleeding. The lad's got scarcely any pulse left." After that there was just a mumble of voices.

Anne came in to sit with Walter. "You're to have the windows wide open," she said, and pushed both sashes up as high as they would go. A raw breeze, smelling of wet earth and wood smoke, rushed in, and with it, faintly, came the rattle of drums.

"The soldiers are going back to the barracks," explained Anne.

The soldiers had been drilling and he had not heard them!

Anne sat down on the little rush-bottomed chair by the fireplace and took her sampler out of her sewing bag. Walter knew that sampler well; she had been working on it for years and the boys were forever hurting her feelings by teasing her about the verse on it.

How sweet it is to see a child,
Tender, merciful and mild,
Ever ready to perform
Acts of kindness to a worm.

It had not been so bad when she was little, but now
that she was growing long and spindly and beginning to
give herself airs, it was too silly for words. It was all
grubby too; if ever she finished it, it would have to be
washed before it was framed. The stuff girls spent their
time on!

She sat with her black-slippered toes set primly together, the skirt of her blue gown drawn modestly down
to her ankles, and her frilly apron spread out over her
lap. A blue velvet snood that matched her eyes and her
dress went round her head and kept her hair in place
over that old scar, but it wasn't of much use against the
raw April breeze that went careering about the room
and loosened a long yellow lock and whipped it across
her cheek. Her little nose was turning pink with cold.
She sighed.

"You mustn't talk, Wattie," she admonished him.

Walter had no wish to talk now. He was straining his
ears toward that low-voiced conversation that was still
going on in the hall.

Dr. Rutherford came back at length to blister him, and
during that unpleasant process he fainted again.

Faces disturbed and anxious, came and went like
shadows in the half-open doorway. Mr. Scott and John,
looking in with heavy silence, James Wilkinson tiptoe-

ing past, Tom hopefully making signs in dumb-show.

"He must have no heavy covers," his uncle said, and swept back over the foot-board of the bed the quilt and comforter, the thick warm blankets, leaving him only a sheet and one light afghan.

"But, Daniel, will he no take cold?"

"I think not, Anne. The weather should be abating any day now. In any case, his blood must not be over-heated, and he cannot bear the weight of all those things."

"Uncle Daniel, how long——"

"Wattie, you must not talk."

"No, sir. But I have to know—how long will I——"

"It is hard to tell now, my boy, but it will be several weeks anyhow."

Several weeks. Several *weeks*. He closed his eyes quickly to hide the tears that came prickling. He could not bide in bed for several weeks. How many were several anyhow? Two would be a couple. If he had meant three, likely he would have said "Two or three." Several must be four, or even five. At the best it was an eternity.

"Dear lad, you are fortunate to be here at all."

They settled him for the night. Both windows were left wide open and the curtains pinned up out of the wind, which stirred a picture hanging on the wall and made the night lamp flicker and flare. The easy chair and footstool from Mrs. Scott's dressing-room were brought in and she settled down, wrapped in a woolen shawl, to watch over him. Tom came in once to get his night things out of the wardrobe and paused by the bed.

"You can have my agate marble," he said, "—don't talk."

It was cold, and that one cover felt like nothing at all. The chill sneaked in around his neck and shivered down his spine. He ached all over.

Several weeks. And twenty-four hours had not gone by yet! It was not fair. A lame leg was enough. He had had a sort of bargain with God; he had taken the leg in his stride, and God for His part ought not to have let a thing like this happen.

He sniffled, and his mother was out of the shadows in an instant and beside him. She sat holding his hand in one of hers and with the other stroking his forehead.

"Puir laddie," she murmured, "puir laddie. But six weeks is no lifetime, though it may seem that to ye now. A stout heart to a steep brae—you've always had that."

Six weeks. Six.

An owl hooted in the Meadows, melancholy and lonely sound.

"The mice and the wee rabbits had best take cover," said Mrs. Scott.

He felt her finger groping for his pulse and it irritated him; he drew his hand away. But he liked the soft, steady touch on his forehead. Over and back, over and back. . . .

When he woke he was stiff and cramped and chilled. One of the curtains had come loose from its pins and was standing straight out in the room. Light flooded every corner, the cold, harsh light of a sunless day. His mother had vanished and in her stead were two withered old dames who lived in Windmill Street and who were called in whenever there was illness or any other sort of emergency.

"I want some brose," said Walter. Thick, hot, strong meat broth that Hannah made so well. That would warm him to his toes.

They were just waiting to souse upon him, he thought disgustedly, the two old ladies, patting their thin gray lips furiously with their wrinkled forefingers. They made little clucks with their tongues against their teeth but said nothing, as if they thought that they too had been forbidden to speak.

His mother brought him the little bit of boiled rice which was to be his breakfast.

"Your uncle says you are not to have any meat," she explained apologetically, "it's too heating."

He could not eat the rice. It burned his mouth and choked him without warming him.

The morning noises of the household went on: Tom and Daniel pounding down the stairs and slamming the front door behind them; Anne singing a snatch of "Auld Robin Gray"; Mr. Scott going into his office and saying "Good morning, Grierson," to his clerk before he closed the door; Jessie breathing heavily over the brass stair rods she was polishing. And outside, the shouts of some lads in the Meadows, the clatter of the pye man's bell in the Square, and more faintly, a fishwife's high-pitched cry of "caller ou."

He rolled his head back and forth despairingly on the pillow.

19

WEARY WEEKS

WALTER yawned. He was alone. Nobody was there to souse upon him at his first word and make him be silent, but then neither was there anyone for him to talk to. It must be mid-afternoon. He had not heard the soldiers pass by on the Meadow Walk, and yet it seemed a long time since he had had his dinner of boiled potatoes and boiled kail. Time *was* long now. Each day was so long that when evening came he could scarcely remember back as far as the morning. And every day was just like every other day. April had gone and May had come, but still the days were gray and wet and cold, and still he lay in bed aching and shivering in a windswept room with one thin blanket drawn up to his chin. Everybody was complaining of the weather and quoting the old saying, "If there's one good day in seven, Sunday's sure to come and lick it up."

There they were! Drums and the pipes and the quick thump of marching feet—the soldiers! He raised himself on his elbow. Oh, if only he could see them! He could see on the ceiling a faint rosy flicker reflected from their scarlet coats, and that was all. Soon it too passed, and the sounds that stirred his pulses died away in the distance. If there were a mirror on the ceiling . . .

He heard the stamp of Daniel's unhurried step upon the stairs.

"Dan! Come here a minute."

The door opened and Daniel's round face appeared at the edge of it, looking a bit startled. "Is anything wrong with you?"

"No, I just want——"

"Oh. You aren't to talk, you know." He came in sidewise, holding something behind him. "Mother told me to come sit with you—she's taking Anne to the mantua-maker's."

"What's the book you've got in your hand?"

"It was a surprise, but I might have known you'd smell it out. Irving sent it to you. Here."

"Vertot's *Knights of Malta*. By jing, that looks like a good one. Where did ye see Irving?"

"He gave it to Tom at the college."

Walter opened the book and looked in, then closed it again. Best save it for later and make the most of Daniel while he had him. If only it had been Tom. But Tom was with Dr. MacFait, having a lesson in mathematics, as Walter would be himself if he weren't stuck here in bed.

"Dan, go get a mirror and a hammer and nail, like a good lad."

"What for?"

"I want to put it up on the ceiling there and catch what's going on in the Meadow Walk."

"Oh. D'you think ye could? Where will I get a mirror?"

"Take that one off the wall yonder."

"Oh." Daniel looked at himself in it; smoothed down his hair with the flat of his hand, retied his narrow black tie, pulled down his bottle-green waistcoat, and brushed a piece of lint from the shoulder of his red jacket. "If I take down that mirror there won't be any looking-glass in the room to see yourself in."

"I don't get the pleasure out of preening myself before a mirror that some callants do."

The shot made no impression on young Daniel. He took the glass down and stood holding it helplessly in his hands and gazing up at the ceiling as if he expected the hook to take wings and fly to plant itself in the new place. "I don't see how I'm to make it stay up there," he said plaintively, and began to make faces at himself in the mirror.

"Oh, away with you and fetch James. And tell him to bring a hammer and nails."

While Daniel was gone Walter followed him in his mind downstairs, imagined him hunting for James, explaining his errand, waiting for James to get the tools, coming upstairs again. They ought to be here now. Of course Daniel never hurried for anyone. He allowed a little more time. Perhaps James was polishing silver or something and would have to finish the piece he was working on before he left. He allowed more time for that. They ought to be here now. If they could just get the mirror fixed before the soldiers came back! By jing, he could have been up and down those stairs a dozen times before this—and he had a lame leg.

Then they were at the door, James in a green baize apron with a hammer in his hand. He understood what was wanted at once, though it took a little while, what with trips for a stepladder and wire and a different sort of hook, to get the mirror in place.

"There!" he said at length, stepping down very well pleased.

"Um-hm, ye-es." There was nothing to see in the Meadow Walk at present but the trees and some urchins, but even so Walter could tell that it wasn't going to work. They showed upside down in the mirror and distorted, stretched out, and indistinct.

James and Daniel came to stand at his bedside, bent over with their head tilted on one side, trying to see the mirror just as he would see it.

"I know what's wrong," exclaimed Walter. "It needs to go at a slant—then it would get the whole scene."

"Ye're richt, Mr. Walter."

So up went James Wilkinson on his ladder again, for more hammering, more bending of hooks and adjusting of wires. But now Walter could not see what was in the mirror at all.

"We need another looking-glass to catch what's in that one."

Tom and John arrived at that moment and the situation was explained to them.

"You need two more mirrors," said John. "One here and one here, and then one over there where Wattie can see it without having to crane his neck. Get the little looking-glass out of my room, Dan. And then we need one more——"

"Take one of Mother's, she won't care. And hurry, Dan."

"I have to do all the work," grumbled Daniel. "Every time I come near Wattie I have to go fetch something for him or move something or——"

"Or something. It's a great pity about you. Step, you lazy chiel."

" 'To seek het water beneath cold ice,' " quoted Walter in high good humor now that he saw it was going to work out as he hoped:

> "Surely it is a great folie—
>   I have asked grace at a graceless face,
>   But there is nane for my men and me."

"Go along, graceless," commanded John. "Get the wide mirror, it will show more."

It took a great deal of adjusting and shifting to get the mirrors rigged exactly right. Anne came in in the middle of it all and demanded to know what was going on.

"Go sew your sampler, monkey, and keep out of busy folks' way," said Tom.

"Wattie wants the mirrors fixed so that he can see the lobsters when they go out to drill," John took time to explain. "How's this, Wattie?"

"A little more this way."

"That?"

"No, the other."

"The *other*, he said."

Everybody was offering suggestions in voices that rose higher and higher, so that Walter, who was the only one who really knew what could be seen from the bed, had to shout to be heard above the rest.

"Bairns! Whatever is all this din about?" Their mother stood in the doorway. A swift silence fell; nobody moved. "Are you clean daft, every one of you? Be off with you this minute."

Abashed and quiet they melted away. James Wilkinson crept back for his hammer, not daring to look at Mrs. Scott. Walter started to speak.

"No, don't say one word. You'll have done more than enough talking for one while." She moved quietly about the room putting it to rights, taking in the arrangement with a quirk of her eyebrow and an amused look about her mouth.

"Here's some wee carved crossbows your Aunt Christian sent you—they're some odd toys she had in her cabinet in the parlor. She thought they might amuse a sick lad who cares about all the trappings of ancient warfare. What's that you have in the bed, a book? You're to do no reading tonight. I'll just put it out of temptation. Lie down and rest and see what you can see in your mirrors, and we'll hope all this shouting and skirling have done you no harm."

Walter lay back on the pillow, feeling suddenly tired and weak. He looked up. There on the wall, like a bit of stage scenery in a gilded frame, was a part of the Meadow Walk. The trees moved a little in the breeze, their branches hazy with little new green leaves, and as he watched, the late afternoon sun suddenly came out and made golden splotches on the walk. A blackbird hopped over the grass. A wee terrier came marching busily along on his short legs, stopped to investigate an insect in the path, and trotted on again out of the mirror, his stiff black tail curving in the air behind him like a handle. It must be too late for the soldiers now, but to-morrow he would see them. Eh sirs, thought Walter, this would be like having a theater in his room.

His supper came in, boiled rice and turnips, and he applied himself to the mess for the first time without thinking yearningly of friar's chicken and crabbie claw and other good things that he might not have.

Before he went to sleep he saw the watchman with his lantern go past along the Meadow Walk, and presently the moonlight lay like snow over the ground and made sharp slim shadows of the trees.

Next morning he watched the soldiers march by, and then he turned to the book that Irving had sent him. It was the history of the long struggle of the Knights of Malta to preserve their island from the Turks, and every few pages there came a diagram showing how the troops or the ships were arranged and how the battles were fought. Using pebbles and buttons for infantry and Miss Chritty's wee crossbows for artillery, he laid out the campaigns among the heaps and hollows of his bed and fought them through during the long silent hours. When he needed something to serve as a fortress he sent word by Tom to a carpenter friend of his in the Candlemaker Row, and presently he had a tiny castle carved out of wood.

It was a childish sort of game, he thought sometimes, but quickly answered himself that he was learning from it all the time. He saw warfare now not in a romantic haze of clashing arms and heroic deeds, but as a science, with problems of strategy and tactics that were as clear and sharp as the bits of a puzzle.

When he finished the *Knights of Malta* he fought through Orme's *History of Indostan* in the same way. If only, he would think despairingly, if only he could have been a soldier! But now he was not only lame but sick and weak as well. Yes, and cold and hungry too, and cross sometimes, but no longer bored.

As soon as he was allowed to have visitors, John Irving came every day to play a game of chess with him. May continued as cold and wet as it had begun, and Irving and Wattie shivered in the blast from the open windows as they moved their men over the board with fingers stiff with cold, or between moves went, chin on fist and brows bent, into long deliberations.

And so it was the weary weeks went by. The day actually came when he was downstairs for dinner, and the day of his first walk in the Square. The mirrors were taken down from the walls of his room. His mother began to talk of Kelso. They packed his things.

This time he stayed with Uncle Robert Scott, who had retired from the East India Company (where young Robert was now) and had bought a place called Rosebank a little out of the town. In the daytime Walter rode all over the countryside on a pony, or perched in one of the trees that overhung the river, shooting at gulls and cormorants as they flew past and eating gooseberries between whiles. In the evenings he and his uncle read ballads together or swapped tales of the ancient borders. Uncle Robert, unlike Father, considered an interest in such things entirely natural and respectable.

20

WRITER'S APPRENTICE

"WALTER, be pleased to step into my office for a few minutes. I wish to speak to you."

"Yes, Father. Now?"

"Better sune as syne, as the saying goes. If you have no other eggs on the spit."

"No, sir." He could change his damp clothes later. The office was warm, with the fire on the hearth.

"Sit down, my lad."

He faced his father over the flat-topped desk and scoured his mind for what might be coming. His record was clear.

"Yes, Father?" he said brightly.

The old gentleman seemed to be having trouble in getting started. He pushed his forefinger up under his bob-wig and rubbed his temple in a perplexed sort of way. The little bit of his own hair that showed was turning white; there were lines about his kind, anxious blue eyes, soft folds under his chin; his ruddy cheeks drooped a little. Father's beginning to show his age, thought Walter, surprised that he had not noticed it before.

"Well, well, March comes in wi' an adder's head and gangs out wi' a peacock's tail."

As he spoke a gust of wind made the panes rattle and sent the curtains bellying out into the room. The peacock was lashing its tail instead of spreading it, thought Walter.

"I saw a young rabbit in the Meadows," he offered aloud in support of the peacock, "and there are snow-drops under the leaves in the garden."

"You'll have been taking a turn in the Meadows?"

"Yes, sir."

"And that is a volume of verses, nae doubt, that is distending your pocket out of all shape?"

Walter pulled it out guiltily and turned it over in his hands—the second volume of Bishop Percy's *Reliques,* much worn.

"Ye may set it on the table yonder and take it with you when you go out. I do not like to see a lad fiddling with something in his hands when I am talking with him. Well, to call another cause, Walter, there's a time for gathering and a time for casting away, and the man of sense will take the gathering time first."

"Yes, sir," said Walter, since an answer seemed to be expected. He wondered uneasily what all this was lead-ing up to.

"You are now fifteen years of age, are you not—or practically fifteen."

"Yes, sir. That is, I'll be fifteen in August." Today was the thirty-first of March. April, May, June, July— four months. He was practically fifteen in the same sense that his mother would say it was practically half-past ten when it was really only seventeen minutes past and he wanted to read another chapter of his book before going to bed.

"We must begin to think of your future. You have been a boy, throwing away time in a boy's pursuits, now you must enter upon the gathering-in period that will be necessary if you are to rise in your profession. Ars longa, vita brevis—to speak somewhat loosely, for the law is no mere art but the most lofty of sciences."

"But, Father——"

"Whisht, you must not interrupt the court. Your vocation will be, of course, the law——"

Robert for the navy—what a pity he had left it, the Scotts were not businessmen—John for the army, Walter for the law. The dull, dry, dusty law. It had always been as much a matter of rote as the charm Anne said over her buttons: "doctor, lawyer, merchant, chief.". . .

"We shall, ultimately, have to consider whether you are to follow in my footsteps as a Writer to the Signet or climb one round higher and seek to acquire the gown of the barrister."

And suppose he should blurt out, "But I don't want to be a lawyer at all?"

He could imagine the aghast silence there would be in the room. His father would ask him to repeat what he had said, as if he could not believe that he had heard aright. The clerk Grierson, sitting like a mouse at his desk in the corner, would forget to pretend not to be listening and would drop his quill that was now squeaking steadily across folio pages. Then Father would begin to talk about the majesty of the law, the uniquely honorable position it occupied in Edinburgh. His voice would sound as usual, but his face would show his hurt. When he had said his say, he would inquire with cold courtesy what Walter proposed to do instead.

And what else could he do? The army would have no use for a lamiter. He did not want to be a minister. He couldn't say, "I'd rather inherit a border peel and live in it," or, "I'd rather be a man of letters." That would sound daft. Irving and Adam were going into the law. Irving was already apprenticed to a Writer.

"Although it is too early to decide whether you are to fill the situation of a Writer or an advocate, it is not too early to——"

"I think I would rather be an advocate, Father."

"Never interrupt the court, Walter."

He had not meant to interrupt, but he knew that he did not want to be a Writer. Father was a Writer. He did all the tedious, necessary, plodding routine work that went on behind the drama of the courts. He did not want his life to be like his Father's.

"The advocate may, it is true, rise to heights impossible for the Writer to aspire to, but on the other hand he may sink to a briefless obscurity. The Writer is sure of a competence. He may not achieve fame, but he will have security."

Security. *Security.* And John could go into the army for danger and for glory.

"I should think that your shyness would be a hindrance

to a successful career at the bar, but as you grow older you may overcome that. In any case, the technical knowledge of the Writer is useful and even essential to the barrister. I think it will be best for you to enter into an apprenticeship now. At the end of the five years you can either become a Writer or go on with your legal studies at the university in preparation for your bar examinations. In either case no time will have been lost. Now how does that appear to you—like a wise course to follow?"

"Yes, Father."

"You would like then, to become a Writer's Apprentice now?"

"I—I would like to please you." The words came out awkwardly, he meant them so hard. It was strange and disturbing to feel about your father, who was so far above you, next to God, as he felt about his. It was, well, almost pity he felt, and a wish to protect him from disappointment. Perhaps because he had just noticed how much older he was looking.

"That is well said, my dear boy, but it is not a question of pleasing the father but of finding the wise course for the son. Grierson, if you will bring me that agreement. We may as well sign it now, Walter, and at the next meeting of the Society of Writers to the Signet we can compear and have it recorded in their minute-book."

The law. Not the law of life and death, but the law of forms and conveyances. Irving would be in Mr. Wauchope's office in the New Town. Adam—oh, if only he and Adam could be fellow-apprentices!

"Shall I be your only apprentice, Father?"

"No, you will have a companion. Mr. Ramsay of Kip-
pilaw has asked me to accept his son James. He is a little
older than you. He was at the college—no doubt you
know him."

"Oh, Jamie Ramsay. Yes, I know him. He plays a good
game at golf and he's full of daffing." He was a cheerful
kind of fellow, but he wasn't Irving or Adam.

"Humph. Golf. Well, *sua quemque trahit voluptas.*
I trust he is not over-waggish—or a novel-reader. That
would be *pessimi exempli* for you. You are a good bairn,
Walter, you have a certain mother-wit, but cultivate
solidity. Solidity, my boy."

He took the quill which Mr. Grierson presented at
his elbow. "An indenture—five years—under a mutual
penalty of forty pounds sterling." Walter Scott, he signed,
under his father's Walter Scott.

"And if I decamp you will have to apply to my father
for the penalty, because I have no forty pounds."

The little joke was not a success. Mr. Scott indicated
fussily that he considered the remark frivolous, and occupied himself with the sanding and folding of the document. Walter moved over to the fire. He was cold. He
had got wetter than he thought out in the Meadows in
that shower.

"Two other matters, Walter—small things both. Copy-
money is the apprentice's perquisite, and the fee is thrippence a page."

By jing, he knew that but he had forgotten it. Apprentices spent long hours copying legal documents, but

they were paid for it. A way to earn some money of his own at last!

"Your hand, fortunately, is much improved, but I wish you would have a care to the crossing of your t's and the closing of your a's at the top. And the other—you will want a nook of your own to study in. I have had the area parlor cleared out for you, and you may consider it entirely your own *sanctum sanctorum* from now on."

"Oh, Father! *Thank* you."

In the glass door of the bookcase across the room he saw his own face, dimly reflected, break up in beams of joy. His father put a hand on his shoulder.

"I am confident that you will never regret what you have done today. Whichever branch of the law we ultimately decide on, I could ask nothing more for you than that you should take your part worthily in a profession that is above all others honorable. How tall you're growing, lad," he broke off to say with the same sort of surprise at a change that had been taking place unnoticed before his very eyes that Walter had felt earlier about him. "That illness of yours, it was a bad business, but I believe you are stronger now than you were before. There ne'er was a loss, as the wise man sayeth, without some small profit."

Walter waited patiently for his father to finish. His Lochaber ax and claymore, he was thinking, he had a place for them now. And the old coins that Mr. Constable gave him. And all the other things that he had been keeping so long in the box under his bed.

As soon as he was released he made a dive for his new

domain. It was a tiny room downstairs with a window
and a door opening on the area, furnished with a desk,
a chair, some bookshelves, and a small cabinet that had
vanished long ago from the drawing-room, painted green
with a faded gilt and vermilion Chinese design on it.
He made trips up and down the stairs until he had as-
sembled all his treasures. His books went on the shelves
—he would have more books as soon as the copy-money
began to flow in—the old coins, the bonnet-piece of
James V, the unicorn of James II, the gold testoon of
Queen Mary, and some Roman coins dug up at Inveresk,
were spread out in the cabinet, the claymore and Lochaber ax he put on the wall, crossed above the little print
of Prince Charlie that his mother had given him. Below
the print he hooked up Broughton's saucer, and stood
back with eyes half shut to survey the result. Very good,
ve-ry good. When he had a fire on the hearth and some
red curtains at the window (maybe Mother had some old
ones) it would look fine indeed.

And it was all his own. Tom could come in when he
wanted to and once in a while he would let Anne in to
dust or fix the curtains, but he would keep meddling
Daniel out altogether. It would be a fine place to write
on the *Conquest of Granada* and read it to Irving when
he came.

If he ever saw Irving any more, or Adam either. When
they were all three indentured to different masters they
would not have the same opportunities to see each other.
Why, they had seen each other every day at the High

School or the college since they were little tinklers.

He sat down at the desk and slowly opened the drawer into which he had stuffed the *Conquest of Granada*. His epic poem. He had written four books so far, each one four hundred lines long.

Walter Scott, Writer's apprentice. What did Writer's apprentices have to do with epic poems? He read down the familiar pages. It wasn't any good anyhow. It was over-elaborate, artificial, bombastic. With sudden decision he thrust it into the fireplace and reached for the flint and tinder.

The top sheets flared up hotly and cast a quick glow over the little room. The edges of the loose pages curled and turned black, the white sheets deepened to pale brown, the writing stood out copper-colored after the paper was no more than an ash, ready to dissolve at a touch. The glow died with a faint crackling noise and he lit it again. There was some smoke, an acrid smell of burnt paper, some poking with the tip of a boot, a last hot flare, and the *Conquest of Granada* was no more. It had no place in his new life—and it had not been good anyhow.

He tipped his chair back and put his feet on his desk. Young Walter Scott, the Writer's apprentice. The industrious apprentice. He helps his father a great deal—the old gentleman has had so much trouble before this with idle apprentices. Yes, his head used to be full of ballads and epic poems and maggots of that sort, but he's put all that aside. He's all for the law now.

Thrippence a page for copy-money. Four pages to a shilling. By jing, he would have to copy only sixteen pages to get enough to buy Evans's collection of ballads that he saw in Creech's window yesterday.

21

THE WICKS OF BAIGLIE

D AWN of an August morning, and the city still asleep.
Up from the wynds and closes the mists left over
from the night curled into the new sunshine. Walter
rode his hired pony down the Candlemaker Row and into
the empty and silent Grassmarket. Far above the tall,
cramped houses, where people still crowded sleeping,
rose the Castle on its rock, touched to unearthly beauty
by the morning light.

It would be a fine day, and he would be in Perth by
nightfall. He rode through the West Port and out into
the Queensferry Road. The Castle, towering now directly over him, threw the road into shadow; the air
was sharp with the chill of the dew-wet rocks and grasses.
A robin sang on a tombstone in St. Cuthbert's kirkyard,
and the crossroads where the Queensferry Road met
the end of Princes Street, usually so busy, were deserted.

Now his journey was really beginning. He cast one
final look behind him at the Castle and settled to his
pony's steady trot.

Tonight he would be in Perth, his first night alone

at an inn, and late tomorrow he would reach Invernahyle, not as a boy visiting an old family friend, but as an apprentice on his master's business. It was immensely exciting to be going north for the first time—alone, and on a pony of his own—and yet he could not help feeling a little nervous lest he make some foolish mistake and reveal himself as an inexperienced boy after all.

He crossed the Water of Leith at the Dean village, and started up the hill on the other side. Eight miles or so now to South Queensferry, and he must be there in time to catch the flood tide. The ferry waited for nobody. This part of the way he knew, Crammond bridge and Crammond Church, Lauriston, and Dalmeny; he and Jamie Ramsay had explored the whole region on foot in their free hours; but beyond the Firth he would be in new country.

The sun was really up now. It laid long fingers across the road and touched the scarlet poppies in the ditch. Bits of thistledown floating in the air caught the sunlight and glistened. The birds were noisy, chattering and calling among themselves.

This time yesterday he was asleep. Why, even last night he and Irving had been walking in the Meadows, their arms over each other's shoulders, chanting the ballad of Cumnor Hall in the moonlight without a thought that today would be anything but an ordinary day full of Dirleton's *Doubts* and Stair's *Decisions,* of forms and contracts and perhaps, if luck was good, a chance of copy-money. And right at the moment when he had been most unconscious of impending destiny, the express had been arriving from Invernahyle and his father had been making arrangements for the trip. When he went in, near bed time, it was all settled. And now here he was!

He patted his dispatch box lovingly. Being an apprentice was not going to be so bad after all, if this sort of thing was likely to happen. And there was the copy-money too. He had bought Evans's *Ballads* with the first fees he had earned, and in the collection was Meikle's "Cumnor Hall," which was, at the moment, his favorite poem. It was the story of Lord Leicester, who married a beautiful young girl and then kept her hidden at Cumnor Hall. He liked the first stanza best.

> "The dews of summer night did fall,
>   The moon, sweet regent of the sky"

He jogged it out in time to the motion of his pony:

> "Silvered the walls of Cumnor Hall
>   And many an oak that grew thereby."

That was what he and Irving had been spouting in the moonlight just last night. And two nights ago—was it possible? yes, Tuesday—had been that embarrassing affair at John Davidson's house.

He had not wanted to go anyhow. For a mere apprentice of a Writer to the Signet to dine with the Keeper of the Signet itself was an awful event, too much of a strain for pleasure. But what could he do when Mr. Constable insisted? And when he got him there, he and Mr. Davidson, the most enthusiastic antiquaries in Edinburgh, talked sixteen to the dozen about castrametation, *prætoria*, and the precise dialect of the Pictish kings, while Walter and young Davidson, who was in the army, stared at each other across the table and said nothing. And then the Pragmatic Sanction coming up and Mr. Constable laughing—laughing, in that house!—and saying:

"Now, John, I'll wad ye a plack that neither of these two lads ever heard of the Pragmatic Sanction."

And the Keeper of the Signet answering in a voice of thunder: "Not heard of the Pragmatic Sanction! I would like to see that!"

It was funny to remember now, but it had been terrible at the time: Mr. Davidson pronouncing the question to his son, and young D. meekly allowing as how he knew nothing about it, and old D. in a towering rage driving him from the table. And he himself taking advantage of the general confusion to depart quietly from the house. Depart? Probably abscond was the word.

Two days ago that, and now this: riding alone to the Highlands with business to transact. And when the business was finished he would hear Invernahyle's stories all over again, especially the ones about Rob Roy, and this time he would know some of the places.

He came to the top of the hill above the Hawes Inn and saw the Firth of Forth spread out before him, the ferry tied up at its wharf, the island of Inchgarvie like a neat little nosegay in the middle of the blue water, and beyond, the shores of Fife with farms running down to the Firth and the Ochil Hills rising behind them.

The little village of South Queensferry was fully

awake. Smoke mounted from the inn chimney, travelers were coming and going, dogs barking, and the men about the ferry-boat shouting to one another. Just after Walter got his pony on board, the diligence from Edinburgh came lumbering down the hill and discharged three passengers. He saw them look curiously at him as he limped to the bow of the boat to see all of the view that he could. Humph. Had they never seen a lamiter before?

It was a marvelously clear day. The air blew fresh from the east over the water. You could see the Bass Rock at the mouth of the Firth, and the Berwick Law; you could see a bit of Edinburgh sitting high on its rock if you looked back. But in front, drawing nearer and nearer, were the shores of Fife and the Ochil Hills and beyond them, too far to see but not too far to reach in a day's ride, the Highlands.

At North Queensferry he took the road to Dunfermline; the same road, he thought, that Queen Margaret and Malcolm Canmore took when they went from their rude little castle on Edinburgh's rock to their palace at Dunfermline.

> The king sits in Dunfermline town,
> Drinking the bluid-red wine

—but that was another king.

He found Loch Leven sparkling in the morning sunshine, and on the island in the center of it, the castle that Mary Stuart knew to her sorrow. What would you give to be that boy, the little Douglas, who helped her to escape? But then you wouldn't be alive now.

They were cutting the corn in the fields and the stubble was red-gold in the sunshine. Poppies blossomed in it, and lapwings gathered in companies.

At the inn at Kinross he stopped to rest and eat. After he left Kinross the country changed. The neat rich farms vanished, and the ground rose in long waste swells like the sea. It had beauty now with the sun on the wide stretches of heather and its fragrance in the breeze and the bees humming in it, the cloud shadows moving swiftly over it, but how desolate it would be in a rain or a mist. Walter thought of the border country with its abbeys and ruined peels, its twisting Tweed, and he felt a little chilled and lonely.

At Damhead he stopped to inquire the way of a blue-gowned gaberlunzie who reminded him of Andrew Gemmels in Kelso.

"Weel now, strictly speaking, there's four roads into Perth, but I'd advise ye to tak' the Wallace Road. It's no the turnpike but it's the shortest, and the oldest. Ye'll go the gate Wight Wallace went wi' his troops to harry King Edward—and they say the Romans bruised their heels on it a many year before Wullie Wallace drew breath, and Cromwell a many year after. Turn tae the left at Hutchbraes Farm and keep going."

Walter put a penny in the old man's wooden bowl and rode on. The village of Damhead dropped quickly behind him; the farmhouse where he turned huddled close to the earth under a lank tree or two and the bare hills mounted steadily before him. These were the Ochils, which he had seen so often from Arthur's Seat and the Castle.

No coaches passed this way any longer, and the road was sinking into disrepair. Walter met a gentleman on horseback coming from the other direction, and passed a tough-looking carle on foot who was just his idea of what a smuggler looked like, but otherwise he saw nobody but a farm-worker or two and a wandering merchant with a pack on his back. The afternoon was wearing on; the sunshine came slanting through the twisted branches of the old trees that now flanked the road on both sides. Ahead at the top of the ridge he could see a sort of niche between the hills. Perhaps that was the Wicks of Baiglie. What had he heard about the Wicks of Baiglie, except that it was a pass over the Ochil Hills between Damhead and Strathearn? His pony plodded slowly up the hill. He was getting tired, poor beast, and Walter himself was beginning to think how glad he would be to reach the inn at Perth.

At the top of the hill he caught his breath and pulled up the reins without intending to.

There, spread out before him was the most beautiful view he had ever seen. Almost beneath his feet the earth fell away and far down below a wide river made silver loops over a green valley; the town of Perth, towered and steepled, stood between its two broad meadows—were those the Inches he had read about?—and beyond—oh, beyond!—were mountains, enormous, blue, unending.

He was seeing the Highlands. He, Walter Scott!

22

THE NEWS

WALTER came into the office and set his staff in a corner—good stout stick, it made walking easier and quicker. He cast a glance over the room. Grierson was writing away at his desk and James Ramsay peered like a sleepy owl over the top of a large leather-bound book which he put down with a thump as soon as he saw that it was only Walter who had come in.

"Well, what news on the Rialto?" said Jamie.

"Where's Father?"

"He's at the courts—didn't you see him?"

"I wasn't there long. He sent me with a message to Mr. Duncan, and on the way back I stopped in—*more meo*—to see Dr. Blacklock."

"Didn't you bring home any news or books or anything to liven things up?"

"It's on-ding of sleet—if that is any news to you. The wind is driving down from Arthur's Seat as if the deil himself were on its tail. Oh, there is some news too. Lauchlan M'Bain has been standing all day in front of the Parliament House windows ringing a bell that would burst your ears if you were as deaf as Ailsa Craig, and doing a brisk business in fly-jacks and toasting-forks."

" 'Nice rrrroasting-toasting jacks!' " Jamie came out with a loud imitation of M'Bain that made Mr. Grierson start. " 'Any more a-wanting my hearty ones? What are you all asleep? Now's your time!' I thought the lawyers paid him a fat sum not to disturb their thoughts—or their slumbers—by calling his wares in their vicinity any more."

"So they did. And he says—the old scamp—that having sold his own tongue to the judges he is under the necessity of using another one, and there he stands clanging his bell loud enough to shiver the balustrades off the Parliament House."

"Can't they hale him into court for disturbing the peace?"

"Your honor, he's juist a puir auld sodger—he really was in the Royal Scots Fusileers—making an honest living selling toasting-forks of his own manufacture, your honor, sir. So they're collecting another fund—to buy off his bell this time."

The apprentices laughed happily over the thought of the old peddler making monkeys out of the reverend lords of the session.

"The old deil," said Jamie affectionately. "I wonder could I make a little pin-money that way. I have a lusty voice too. I could go up the Back Stairs from the Cowgate chanting my wares, any old wares——"

"You aren't a veteran of Culloden."

"True. Eh sirs, what a long day this is. You say it's

sleeting. Did you go to Sibbalds's for the second volume of *Pamela?*"

"It wasn't in."

"That's the trouble with a circulating library. Somebody else always has what you want. What's that book you've got?"

Walter slid it over the desk. *"Don Quixote."*

"The things you read! You begin at the end and then turn to the middle—and what beats me is that when you've finished with the book in your hop-skip-and-jump style you've got more of the meat of it than somebody else beginning at the beginning and reading every word. Did you know this was in Spanish?"

Walter, standing in front of the fire, smiled benignly. "Yes, Cervantes had a way of writing in Spanish," he said mildly.

"Ye donnard eediot! I mean, can you read it?"

"I worry it out with a dictionary. It's good."

"You're welcome to it. Give me a modern domestic novel."

"Yes—Jenny and Jerry Jessamy! I detest the whole tribe."

"Sua quemque trahit voluptas, as your father would say. Let's have a game of chess."

"Now?"

"Now. *Quam primum* and *peremptorie.* We'll just have time before your father gets back." Jamie, his thin dark face suddenly alight with interest, fished under some legal papers in a drawer for the board and chessmen.

"Dr. Blacklock says he's found a poet, the finest poet

we've had in Scotland since William Dunbar. Keep us, this fire is hot! I'm burning my breeks."

"Small loss to the legal profession if you burned the whole suit. It's ready for the rag-bag."

"I know it is, but I like it. I don't know why, but clothes aren't comfortable till they're old."

"Your turn to have the white men. I don't like old clothes. When I'm a Writer I'm going to dress elegantly and be point-device in everything."

"Mr. Dugald Stewart read Dr. Blacklock three of this man's verses and he says they're the purest poetry—all written in Scots, too. He's writing to Dr. Lawrie about them. He thinks an edition would go well in Edinburgh."

"They're unpublished then? Your move, Wattie. Put this nipperty-tipperty poetry rubbish out of your mind and get down to business."

"Some little printer in Kilmarnock published them," said Walter imperturbably, and advanced his king's knight. "His name is Burns and he's a ploughman."

"Must do neat printing." Jamie cackled and took Walter's queen's bishop.

"Burns is not the printer, he's the poet." Walter frowned over the board. He hadn't had his mind on the game and Jamie had got away with that bishop. Now he would have to change his whole plan of attack.

In his corner Mr. Grierson cleared his throat. "That will be Robbie Burns, will it not, Mr. Walter?"

"I don't know his first name. He's from Ayrshire. D'you know him?"

"The last time I was in Mauchline everybody was

laughing over a satiric piece of his, 'The Holy Fair.' He has some reputation as a poet throughout the neighborhood. And other ways too. He's gone—or is just going—to Jamaica, to start a new life there and make his fortune. They say he was to have indented himself for his passage-money, but he's made enough out of his book of poems to pay his way steerage."

"Your move again, Wattie. That will be a sair dunt to Dr. Blacklock—his precious poet flitting to the West Indies just after he's discovered him. What's the matter —is the sheriff after him?"

"How old is he, Mr. Grierson? What's he like?"

"I should say he was twenty-seven or thereabouts, Mr. Walter. Likely he's a better poet than he is a farmer. He—— Whisht, there's your father's step on the stair."

Into the drawer in a single long-armed sweep went chessmen and chessboard. When Mr. Scott appeared in the doorway he found the office steeped in silence; the only sound to be heard was the squeak of Mr. Grierson's pen and the soft rustle as one of the studious apprentices turned a page of the thick volume in which he was engrossed.

"Humph," said Mr. Scott.

As his father settled down at his own desk Walter unobtrusively reversed his copy of Sir James Stewart's *Dirleton's Doubts and Questions upon the Law of Scotland Resolved and Answered,* which he had been studying upside-down. His conscience poked him a little about the deception, but then, he comforted himself, he was not really proving to be "A clerk foredoomed his father's soul to cross." He did everything that his father gave him to do and did it properly. Not that the old gentleman would admit it to him, for fear, no doubt, of encouraging him unduly, but he had told Mrs. Scott, who told Walter, that the boy was really being of material assistance to him. And merciful heavens, everybody needed a little recreation now and then. Even Mr. Scott himself, Walter suspected wickedly, over there in his big chair at this very minute was rioting over his favorite Spottiswoode's *Sermons* instead of attending to the ancient town laws of Scotland.

If John Irving or Adam Ferguson had been his fellow-apprentice he would have written the naughty thought on a piece of paper and slipped it over to him, but he would not laugh at his father, even thus affectionately, with Jamie Ramsay. There was a difference.

"The veteran of Culloden," said Mr. Scott suddenly with a dry smile, "is now bellowing his toasting-forks outside of Bailie Creech's bookshop. It will be interesting to see what the Bailie will do about that. So far as I know there is no *remedium juris*."

"*He*'ll never pay him to go away," exclaimed Walter. "He's too penurious."

"Penurious? That's a very harsh word. If we pay attention to our own faults, Walter, we shall all of us have enough to keep us busy without sitting in judgment on other folks."

"Yes, sir," said Walter, and pretended not to see Jamie Ramsay, behind his book, wiggling his ears at him.

23

MRS. COCKBURN'S SUPPER

THE note had read: "Mrs. Cockburn puts Miss Scott and Mr. Walter in mind that unparaleled brose is ready for them on Monday, 9th, in the mansion of their friend,—A. Cockburn.

"P.S. Cannot spell unparaleled."

It was a clear January evening when they set forth. The frosty moonlight was far brighter than the smoky yellow flames that flickered in the street lamps, and the rocky top of Arthur's Seat was pale against the star-spattered sky.

"I wonder if Mr. Burns will be there," said Anne.

"Mr. *Burns?* Not a chance of it."

"Well, he goes everywhere," returned Anne defensively.

"If he were, we wouldn't be invited. Nobody is going to waste a lion like him on young fry like us."

"Mrs. Cockburn would."

Dr. Blacklock had not. The poet had gone to his house for breakfast, and he had recited his unpublished piece, "Farewell to the Banks of Ayr," standing with his face toward the window and looking out as he repeated

in a plain, slow, forcible voice the affecting lines that
were now familiar all over Edinburgh:

> Bonnie Doon, sae sweet and gloamin',
>> Fare thee weel, before I gang!
> Bonnie Doon, where early roamin'
>> First I weaved the rustic sang.

He must have written it when he thought he was leaving Scotland forever—his passage engaged for Jamaica,
his chest on the way to Greenock—before Dr. Blacklock's
letter had come and brought him instead post-haste to
Edinburgh.

Walter had heard about that breakfast party, but he
had not been there. The little room had been crowded
with the great, the Earl of Glencairn, Lord Monboddo
and his daughter Elabeth, the Honorable Henry Erskine,
Mr. Blair, and Mr. Hume and the rest. Naturally it
had not entered the mind of anyone to invite a Writer's
apprentice who happened to be fond of poetry. . . .

"Well, you can take my word for it, he won't be at
Mrs. Cockburn's."

In spite of himself, however, when the door of the
"mansion" was opened, he could not help casting a
quick glance over Mrs. Cockburn's shoulder into the
parlor to see who was there. Nobody but Miss Henrietta
Cummings.

"Bairns! It is a joy to see you!" Mrs. Cockburn was
greeting them. "Anne, you are bonnier every time I set
eyes on you, and Wattie, how you have grown, lad! And
how buirdly you're getting!"

He felt entirely too big and clumsy for the little room. He was taller than anybody else in it, and the furniture was scaled to their size. He sat down in a chair too small for him and drooped his long hands between his knees. His wrists showed below his sleeves and his coat felt too tight over his chest.

"Is he no a big thing?" said Anne maternally. She was very much devoted to him and had recently developed an irritating way of making comments about him before his face. "He can walk thirty miles in a day and not even get tired. He and Jamie Ramsay and two other lads walked to Prestonpans before breakfast, spent the whole day looking at the ruins and the battlefield, and walked back in the evening."

"Not in this weather, I hope," said Mrs. Cockburn. "I think the cold will congeal my blood. I hardly knew I existed last week except for the exertion of coughing and blowing my nose."

The little parlor was bright with firelight and candles in silver stands. The neat mahogany chairs with covers worked in faded tent-stitch, the Queen Anne china, the Indian screen with Harlequin and Columbine, even the big yellow tabby-cat on the hearthrug looked just as they had always looked during the years that Walter had been coming to see Mrs. Cockburn. The big spinning-wheel in the corner was the only thing that had not always been there. That had appeared several years ago in that sad time after Mrs. Cockburn's only son Adam, who had been a captain of Dragoons, died. Walter remembered how grief-stricken she had been and

how distressed his mother had been about her. The
spinning-wheel had been brought into the parlor then
and the poor lady would stand beside it spinning until
she had made herself too tired to think. Or you met her
out walking in the Meadows, walking through the rain
with a set face, seeing nothing, going nowhere, just getting tired. "A veteran in sorrow," she used to say of
herself.

She was blithe enough now, sitting with her feet on
a little stool, her auburn hair showing through the black
lace hood she wore tied under her chin, her eyes bright
and her head tilted in the spunky little way she had.

"And what," she said, "do you think of our 'heaven-
taught ploughman,' as Henry Mackenzie called him
in the *Lounger* last month?"

"I've only seen him from a distance. One day he came
into Sibbalds's when I was there." He had hung around
Baxter's Close where Burns was lodging in hopes of
seeing him go in or out, and he had made errands that
took him past Johnny Dowie's tavern where the poet
went often for the Nor' Loch trout or Welsh rabbit
for which the place was known, but he had not got so
much as a glimpse of him, and then one day when he
was poking about among the heaps of old Italian and
Spanish books at the back of Sibbalds's Circulating
Library, there was a little stir in the front of the shop,
someone hissed "There's Burns," and he caught sight—
a glisk and a glimmer and no more—of his departing
back.

"You haven't met him!" She raised her hands. "I

didn't imagine there was a person left in all Edinburgh who did not profess to know him well. I have never seen this town so agog about anyone. The word has gone out that he will be at the Hunters' ball tomorrow, and all women and all milliners are mad. There's not a gauze cap in Auld Reekie to be had under two guineas and many of them are ten or twelve."

"Wattie would give the world to meet him," said Anne, in her rôle of her brother's interpreter. "But we don't know many of the literary folk or the West Country gentry, and those are the two sets he is most with."

"Father's clerk Grierson knows him," said Walter as if Anne had not spoken, "and he has promised to have him for dinner at his lodgings and invite me too, but he hasn't been able so far to find a day when he wasn't engaged."

"He was at Lady Bal's for tea a week since. The place was full of the literati and the eaterati—and by the by, in spite of the vast numbers of distinguished folk who were there, we sorely missed Lady Anne Lindsay and Lady Elizabeth. They were born with minds, Wattie, which is not nearly so common as is vulgarly supposed. What was I talking about? Oh, yes, the ploughman poet. He receives adulation with native dignity. He is the very figure of his profession, strong and coarse, but he has a most enthusiastic heart of love. He has seen the Duchess of Gordon and all the gay world, and his favorite for looks and manners is Bess Burnett—no bad judge indeed."

"I heard," said Miss Henny Cummings, "that he said she was the most heavenly of all God's works."

"No doubt he did. He well might. How a man who looks the way Lord Monboddo does, a man who thinks our ancestors had tails, could ever be the father of a girl of such grace and sweetness—yes, and beauty—I can't conceive. What's this I hear about the naughty apprentices making sport of Lord Monboddo's racial theories, Wattie?"

"They walk behind him and pretend to be careful not to step on his caudal appendage," said Walter absently, thinking still of the poet Burns.

"Tuts. And tell Henny what happened in the affair of Bailie Creech and the Veteran of Culloden."

"Oh, the Bailie brought M'Bain before the Dirt Court, and M'Bain produced his discharge from the army and asserted the right it gave him to pursue his calling in any town or city of Great Britain except Oxford or Cambridge. So the Bailie had to dismiss the complaint. Whereupon he took up his stand outside the bookshop and bawled his wares louder than ever. In the end the Bailie had to dig down in his pocket and buy him off."

"Eh sirs, I'll wad ye that went hard with our friend Mr. Creech. Still, he can afford it well enough. I understand he is to bring out the new edition of Burns's poems and that they have fifteen hundred subscribers already."

"Alison, do ye no think it is time for supper?" said Miss Cummings in a sepulchral voice.

"To be sure. Ring, Wattie; you are nearest the bell. We will now have one of Mrs. Cockburn's famous petits soupers, about which the lines in *Stella* might have been expressly written:

> "A supper like her mighty self,
>   Four nothings on four plates of Delf."

On their way home Anne said sympathetically, "I declare, Wattie, I'm growing very weary of hearing about this man Burns. I think he's becoming very tiresome."

Walter put his arm around her. "You're a sonsy lass," he said affectionately, and added in the tone of one who is imparting news, "but I would like to meet him."

24

—AND DR. FERGUSON'S DINNER

D ROP in at Kamschatka this evening," said Adam after church. "Some people are coming for dinner and Mr. Burns will be there."

Dr. Ferguson's friends called Sciennes Hill House Kamschatka because it was so far out of town. It stood on the south side of the Meadows and looked over toward Edinburgh.

Walter dressed for the occasion with more care than he usually bestowed upon the process, in a suit that he had not yet had time to outgrow. He was thinking as he settled his collar just what he would say if he really had a chance to talk to the poet. "I admire your verses profoundly, sir." Who else would ever have thought of writing a poem about a fieldmouse—"Wee sleekit, cow'rin', tim'rous beastie"—who else but a ploughman. And what other ploughman could write with such perfection.

What extremes the man had known! From the wind-swept spaces of an Ayrshire farm to a crowded close in the Old Town, with its cramped quarters and unsavory smells, and from the lodging there, for which he paid one and six a week and shared a deal table, a sanded floor, and a chaff bed with another man, to the most elegant drawing-rooms in the city, where the most distinguished people in Scotland gathered around to praise him. No, probably Walter would not have any personal talk with him, but he would be in the same room with him for a whole evening, and he could watch him and hear what he said.

Sciennes Hill House was square and plain, with three shields under a molding on the front, and the date, 1741, when it had been built. Yet for all its plainness, light shone from the windows and it had the look of a house in which something festive was happening. Principal Robertson's house on one side of it, and Mr. Cockburn's on the other were silent, dim, ordinary in comparison.

As soon as he touched the knocker the door opened and Adam pulled him in. "Leave your hat and great-coat in the hall—drop them anywhere—they're just coming up from dinner."

They kept fashionable hours here, dinner at five o'clock. He felt as if he had stepped into another world. At home they were listening in weary silence now while Father read sermons aloud to them; here there was nothing at all to show that it was the Sabbath. The voices on the stairs coming up from the dining-room below were entirely cheerful.

Principal Robertson was the first one into the parlor. He walked in as if he were heading a procession of the entire faculty of the university. His enormous wig was freshly powdered and curled; his little black hearing-trumpet, fastened by a black ribbon to a buttonhole of his coat, was in his hand; his clerical bands were stiff and white beneath his huge, projecting chin. There was something portentous about him. No wonder his own sisters always addressed him as "sir." Behind him were Dr. Hugh Blair with the elder Miss Ferguson, and Mr. Dugald Stewart with the second one. And after them, between Dr. Ferguson and Mr. John Home, the author of *Douglas,* came Mr. Robert Burns.

He was dressed, as Walter had heard that he would be, in a style midway between that of a farmer on a holiday and that of the company in which he found himself: in a coat with a heavy roll collar and wide lapels, a light waistcoat, and fawn-colored breeches. He wore top-boots instead of silk stockings and pumps, and his own thick dark hair instead of a tie-wig. But what made him stand out among them all, thought Walter, was his eyes. They were deep-set dark eyes, and they glowed; they literally glowed. You knew as soon as you saw those eyes that here was a man who was apart from and beyond all others. There was fire, and spirit, poetry itself, in those eyes.

Principal Robertson began handing around his gold snuff-box set with diamonds, which the Empress of Russia had given him because of the impressive books he had written. The celebrated Mr. Dugald Stewart, who taught Moral Philosophy brilliantly in the university and maintained an elegant figure withal, engaged Mr.

Burns in an aside. Walter could not hear what they were saying, but he saw that they were both laughing over it. Dr. Ferguson went to the thermometer to see if the temperature was as it should be. Walter saw his daughters stealing glances at each other and looking relieved when he turned away without making any comment. Ever since he had had that stroke several years ago he had been abnormally chilly.

It was hard to see in this bent, white-haired, gray-clad old gentleman the young man he had once been, the chaplain to the Black Watch who was adored by his men because of his courage and tenderness. The man who refused to stay in the rear with the surgeons when the battle was on, and when his commanding officer reminded him that his commission did not entitle him to be in the position he had assumed, replied, "Damn my commission, sir," and threw it at him. Well, he was still fiery as gunpowder—that at least was left.

Adam drew Walter down on a bench by the wall.

"What do you think of him?" he whispered.

"Marvelous eyes."

"Yes, hasn't he."

The company settled down in chairs to its various liking, and the conversation centered around the guest of honor. They talked of poetry, English and Scottish, and the young ploughman spoke his opinions modestly but confidently. When Robert Fergusson's name came up he waxed enthusiastic. He had recently, at his own expense, erected a memorial in the Canongate church-yard to the young poet who died in poverty and ob-

scurity, and he spoke of him with humility as his model.
From him he went on to Allan Ramsay.

The boys sat on their bench, silent and unnoticed,
listening with all their ears. Walter thought Mr. Burns's
knowledge of English poetry was rather limited, and
he was surprised to hear him extolling Fergusson and
Ramsay so highly. Was he deficient in critical judgment
—or was he posing a little?

"He's got twenty times the ability of Fergusson and
Ramsay," he whispered to Adam. "He's got genius."

Adam grinned back. "That's what everybody says—
now."

"Well, but he *has*."

They bumped each other's shoulders. Oh, how he
liked being here! He looked sidewise at Adam, at his
dark curly hair, his wide forehead, his alert eyes and
mocking mouth. It was good to be with Adam again,
after so much of Jamie Ramsay.

Mr. Burns rose and went to examine a print that was
lying on the table. Everybody crowded around him to
see it too.

"It's that thing of Bunbury's," said Adam. "You know
—soldier dead on snow, dog looking mournful on one
side of him, widow with child in arms on other. There
are some verses underneath it—I don't remember what."

Mr. Burns held the print up and read the lines aloud:

"Cold on Canadian hills or Minden's plain,
    Perhaps that parent wept her soldier slain;
    Bent o'er her babe, her eye dissolved in dew;

The big drops mingling with the milk he drew
Gave the sad presage of his future years,
The child of misery baptized in tears."

He read well, simply and with feeling. Then Walter saw to his surprise that the poet was genuinely affected, whether by the picture or the verse or perhaps by the ideas which they awoke in his own mind. Tears actually stood in his eyes.

"Whose lines are those?" he asked. "Can anybody tell me who wrote those moving words?"

The literary gentlemen looked blank. Mr. Dugald Stewart frowned and snapped his finger impatiently as if he knew the name perfectly but it eluded him just for the moment. A silence fell.

"They're written by one Langhorne," murmured Walter negligently to Adam.

Adam nodded toward Mr. Burns. "Tell him," he whispered.

Walter hesitated. It was such a very august assemblage.

"Mr. Burns," said Adam, "young Scott here says they're by Langhorne. From what poem, Wattie?"

" 'The Justice of the Peace.' "

They all turned round in some surprise to look at Walter. He felt the color mounting in his face.

Mr. Burns himself fixed on him a look of half-serious interest and said warmly: "Thank you. You'll be a man yet, sir."

The conversation immediately whirled away to topics in which the learned gentlemen present were not likely

to be caught napping, at a loss for a name. Walter sat
on in a sort of maze, glowing with pleasure. Robert
Burns, the poet. He would tell his grandchildren about
this.

The verse that had always been a sort of talisman for
him rose in his mind.

> The Lord and Lady of Harden,
> Betwixt them procreat was a son;
> Named William Boltfoot of Harden.
> He did survive to be a MAN!

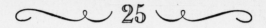

25

WILL CLERK

WALTER made a neat flourish at the bottom of the long legal page, added it to the pile of manuscript, and took another sheet. The flourish was to prevent a forger from inserting material of his own between the last line of one page and the first one of the next. That was the one hundred and nineteenth flourish he had made to-day. He looked at the document he was copying: one more page and he would be finished.

His hand went traveling steadily over the sheet almost as if it worked by itself. His eye, glancing up, counted the lines to come. It was hard to believe that he was within fifteen lines of accomplishing the enormous task he had set himself, to copy the whole brief in a single sitting. He was going strong now; he could have finished it if there had been five or ten pages more.

An hour back he had thought he would have to give in, to put down his pen for the day and leave the final pages until tomorrow. His hand had been cramped and aching, pains shot up his arm into his shoulder, there had been a tired place in the small of his back that was sore to the touch. But he had summoned all his resolution and with it a fresh surge of strength had come, even more than he needed.

He wrote the final word and put down his quill. Leaned back in his chair and stretched his arms as high above his head as they would go. Flexed his long fingers, stiff and aching now, the thumb and forefinger flattened at the ball, the nails grimed with ink.

A hundred and twenty folio pages in a single day! At thrippence a page. That would be thirty shillings, the most money all his own he had ever had at one time. His father kept him shorter than the other lads' fathers did.

He could do a great deal with thirty shillings. He looked at the bookshelves which his books only half filled when he first moved into this den two years ago. Now they were overflowing and there were books on the floor. Copy money had done that. But he had never copied so long at a stretch before. Suddenly he knew that he had to get out into the open. He had been indoors all day. He needed to feel the wind in his face, to breathe the air from the Pentlands and the Firth, to be where people were.

He stacked the pages neatly and put them in order to be delivered tomorrow, took his staff, and went out the door and up the area steps to the street. It was a September twilight; the leaves of the trees were looking a little yellow and dry; the hunter's moon rode enormous over Arthur's Seat.

He heard shrill yells and shouts, the thud of feet on the stone pavements, the clatter of assorted missiles.

The George Square boys were retreating in disorder before the Potterrow loons. Walter recognized the smallest Cumming from next door, stockings around his ankles, legs scratched and bruised, nose streaming blood, running for home as fast as he could go. Close on his heels was a tatterdemalion screeching horridly and reaching out to grab his flying coat-tails.

Walter caught the Potterrow lad by the shoulder and held him. "Run, Andy, run! I'll keep him till ye get inside!"

He looked down at the tough little chiel wriggling in his grip and kicking at his shins with horny brown bare feet. Hard and ferret-faced he was, with the too-knowing look of the city street urchin, but there was something pathetic about his eyes, and the bones of his shoulders under Walter's hand felt much too near the surface. He was thin, as if he did not have enough to eat. Amazing, thought Walter, that he had ever been small enough himself for such lads to seem to him big and fierce. Even Daniel now was too old for bickers.

He released the boy. "Away home wi' ye now," he said. "It's all over for today."

The Milnes' man servant was running off three more invaders from the Potterrow, and Donald, very brave now, was assisting him with a final clod or two. Lights began to appear in the gray houses, and the moon was growing redder as the sky deepened around it and purple shadows gathered in all the corners.

Walter went on toward the High Street, thinking of Green-Breeks. He had been altogether a different sort

of fellow from the little scamp he had held just now by
the shoulder. There had been good material in Green-
Breeks. To look at, he had been the very figure of a
young Goth, with his blue eyes and yellow hair, his tall,
well-built body—and how staunch he had been!

No one knew where he had vanished. By the time
Walter and Tom had got up their courage, several years
after the famous bicker, to tell their father about him,
he had gone. They had made inquiries, for Mr. Scott
would have done something for him, but the old woman
he lived with had died, and Green-Breeks had gone
away, none of the neighbors knew where. Too bad.

Walter paused on the South Bridge to look down into
the Cowgate below, a narrow cañon teeming with people who wore, even when seen from a distance, the unmistakable look of poverty and squalor. Strange to think
that the Cowgate had once been a fashionable suburb.
No doubt the Canongate and the High Street would go
the same way, when everybody had moved over into the
New Town.

The clock of the Tron kirk struck the half-hour over
his head as he came out into the High Street and met
the wind that was sweeping down from the Castle. While
he stood there hesitating as to which way to turn, he
heard a voice sing out:

"Upon my word, man! I thought at first you were a
bogle!"

He swung around and faced Will Clerk, Irving's
cousin whom he had been hearing about for years but
had never met until yesterday in the Civil Law class

which he had just entered. He had liked Clerk from
the moment he saw him. He had something: keen eyes
and a generous mouth, an air of strength and spirit, a
way of laughing.

"That outfit you're wearing would frighten the
bairns!"

Walter looked down at his old corduroy breeches,
bagging at the knees, spattered with ink stains, worn
shiny at the side by the rubbing of his staff. He laughed.

"They be good enough for drinking in," he said,
flourishing his stick, "let's go and have some oysters in
the Covenant Close."

Everybody was going to oyster cellars now. It was the
fashionable thing to do. They turned into a dark passageway and plunged down some steps to the oyster tavern
that was most popular at the moment. Walter bumped
his head on the low door going in and rubbed it ruefully; he was not accustomed yet to being so big.

It was still early and the place was empty. They sat
down at a well-scoured deal table, and presently great
platters of raw oysters and big tankards of porter appeared before them. The candle flames ducked and flared
in the draft; pewter and copper vessels on shelves
along the walls shone in the yellow light. Will Clerk's
bushy eyebrows made shadows on his face; his eyes shone
with friendliness.

"This was a good idea of yours," he said, lifting his
tankard. "Here's to our better acquaintance." And added
confidentially, "You know, when I first saw you yesterday I thought you looked like an hautboy player."

That amused Walter. "Nobody ever accused me before of being even remotely musical. I can't carry a tune
in a knapsack. Probably my long upper lip made you
think of it."

"No; I don't know what it was—something about you.
These are good oysters. John told me about you. We
ought to have known each other long ago."

"Your father is the Sir John Clerk who is supposed
to have discovered the tactics that Rodney used so suc-
cessfully at Dominica, isn't he?"

"Yes. Naval Tactics Clerk, we call him in the family.
As a matter of fact, Rodney had a copy of his book in
his possession before the battle."

"Funny—my brother fought in that battle."

It seemed a striking coincidence. They called for more
oysters.

"That's an interesting stick of yours," said Will,
weighing it in his hand while they waited.

"Got it in the Highlands. Invernahyle gave it to me.
I did some business for him last summer—or rather, for
his brother-in-law."

"You look as if you'd thought of something funny."

"I was to enforce a legal instrument against some
tenants of Stewart of Appin. Appin thought the Maclar-
ens—that was their name—might put up a fight, and so
he got me an escort of a sergeant and six men from a
Highland regiment lying at Stirling. I rode forth with
a front and rear guard with loaded arms!"

Will Clerk whistled. "A Writer's apprentice leading
a military expedition! Did you get into battle?"

"No, it was very flat. When we reached Invernenty the place was deserted—the tenants had gone to America. We spent the night there, ate up what provisions they had left behind, and came back next day. But, man, that sergeant was a character! He was chock-full of stories about Rob Roy."

"Rob Roy MacGregor—the fellow that stole from the rich and gave to the poor?"

"The same. He looked like a Highland bull, this fellow said, with curly red hair and enormously wide shoulders——"

The scuffle of feet sounded on the stairs and the confusion of fresh voices. Another tall lad bumped his head against the door and two more laughed at him.

"Hullo!" said Will. "There's Abercrombie and Cranstoun and Pat Murray of Ochtertyre—d'you know them? Well, you must. They're future barristers, but they have literary interests too. Oh, Patrick!"

Walter rose. They pushed the chairs closer together, dragged others from near-by tables. Fresh platters of oysters, more tankards of porter were brought. The lad they called Cranstoun was being noisily enthusiastic about a new German poem he had read.

From that evening life slowly, indefinably changed. Doors opened and walls fell away. It was partly, Walter knew, because he himself was seventeen and had suddenly come into the fullness of his strength, but it was also because Will's friends, who became his friends, looked out on wider horizons than any he had known.

The law was not to be all of their life. They were cultivating general literature and philosophy and science as well without the least idea that anybody could possibly consider such pursuits as interfering with the proper study of the law.

26

THE FOOTPATH WAY

THE Club came out of a fishing expedition to the Moorfoot Hills.

Walter and George Abercrombie, Adam, and Irving, and Will, set out on foot in the early morning. Three miles an hour was their pace. They tried four miles first, but that was a little too fast for Walter. By leaning on his staff with one hand and resting the other on Will's shoulder, he could keep going at three miles an hour as long as anybody could.

They marched along the lanes between the hawthorne hedges singing Autolycus's song:

> "Jog on, jog on, the footpath way,
>   And merrily hent the stile-a,
> A merry heart goes all the day,
>   Your sad tires in a mile-a,"

and by two o'clock they were in Howgate, and a little later they were fishing in the lake above the town and the stream that flowed into it from the Esk.

They spent the night in a little inn kept by Mrs. Margaret Dodds, where they were the only guests, and pervaded the place, blowing the peat fire, ringing the bell, calling for their meals when the whim struck them, and coming and going through the windows in preference to the door. Next day they fished before breakfast and after breakfast and all through the afternoon. The following morning their landlady, outspoken, unamused, said to them:

"Ye've been here long eneuch now. Awa' hame to yer mithers."

They laughed as they gathered their tackle together. They had planned to go back today anyhow. George and Adam started ahead, and being the faster walkers were soon out of sight in a fold in the hills.

"I say," exclaimed Will, stopping short with the force of his thought, "we aren't far from Pennycuik House. We really oughtn't to go back to Edinburgh without stopping there."

Pennycuik House was the seat of his family. Irving knew it well, but Walter had never seen it. So off they went light-heartedly to Pennycuik.

Never had Walter seen so charming a house. Books, pictures, music, gardens—and Sir John and Lady Clerk perfectly delighted with their visit and overwhelming them with kindness. It was all so gay and so easy, so spontaneous.

Sir John was a tall, striking-looking old gentleman with grizzled hair and a strong Scots accent, and he was as enthusiastic an antiquary as Mr. Constable himself. He showed Walter with great pride a mutilated clay head which, he said, was a Roman antiquity found on the very grounds of Pennycuik house. Walter exclaimed over it with awe and wonder until Will took him aside and whispered that his brother John had manufactured it himself for a joke and nobody dared now to tell their father the truth about it because he had boasted of it everywhere and the Earl of Buchan admired it so much that he was threatening to carry it off and present it to the Scottish Society of Antiquaries.

Sir John had also a fleet of wee toy boats which he set afloat on the garden pool to demonstrate Rodney's tactics at Dominica—which, of course, were really his own tactics. Walter, with Will's connivance, purloined one of the little boats to take home and put in the cabinet in his den.

The idea of the Club was born the second night of their visit. They all belonged to a literary society already, for which they produced, with great effort and a mammoth display of learning, the most serious papers; but this was to be different. Less erudition and more high jinks. They would meet in a room in Carrubbers Close every Friday evening and afterwards adjourn to a nearby oyster cellar for refreshments. They talked over all their friends and decided whom they would invite to belong. Adam, of course, and Pat Murray of Ochtertyre —yes, and Pat Murray of Simprim too—and George Abercrombie and George Cranstoun, of course. Davy Douglas—would he fit in? And how about James Edmonstone? They chose names for themselves, and decided that Walter, in memory of his first meeting with Will, his corduroy breeches, the oyster cellar and his passion for things military, should be known as Colonel Grog.

The next day it occurred to them to go home.

Walter found the household at Number 25 George Square in a state of consternation that amounted to frenzy. Adam and George had gone on straight to Edinburgh from Howgate, and not knowing that the others were making a detour to Pennycuik, reported that they were close behind. When they failed to come home that day, or the next, the Scotts were beside themselves with anxiety. Walter was full of compunction over having caused so much distress and resolved to be very careful and precise about his plans in the future.

The next time it happened, he and Will and Adam found themselves at nightfall thirty miles from Edinburgh without so much as sixpence among them.

"Here's a pretty kettle of fish," said Adam. "What do we do now?"

"We walk back," said Walter. "And if Willie is hungry he can eat hips and haws."

"Willie is starved. And to think I had more supper last night than I could eat—and never thought to slip a bite into my pocket!"

Luckily the June night was not too cold. They rested uncomfortably in a haystack and as soon as the early light came they started the tramp home, hollow and worn and pale, but somewhat elated in spite of everything. They asked now and then at a cottage door for a drink of water and more often than not the good wife, seeing how weary they looked, gave them milk instead. And so they won home.

Mr. Scott met Walter at the door, his uneasiness turning to impatience as soon as he saw the prodigal safe.

"So ye got back," he said. "Well, I should like fine to know how ye managed to stay away so long without a penny to your name. I know well ye had no money for I've given ye none since ye felt called upon to cast all of your funds in one throw for a single book of poems. You're not beholden to anyone for your expenses? That would never do. Then what have you been living on these two days?"

"Pretty much like the young ravens," replied Walter cheerfully. "I only wished that I had been as good a player on the flute as poor George Primrose in the *Vicar of Wakefield*. If I had his art I'd like nothing better than to tramp like him from cottage to cottage over the world."

This was too much for the Writer to the Signet. "I doubt, I greatly doubt, sir," he said angrily, "you were born for nae better than a gangrel scrape-gut!" and stamped into his office, slamming the door behind him.

The day came, however, when they stopped worrying about him. He had taken Tom with him, and Mr. Scott said to Mrs. Scott, who was nervous about the younger boy,

"My dear Annie, Tom is with Walter this time, and have you not yet perceived that wherever Walter goes he is pretty sure to find his bread buttered on both sides?"

Walter took a deep satisfaction in his ability to keep up with the others on these long and sometimes taxing jaunts; how deep—and why—he did not realize until one evening when he and Will were walking up the High Street from Carrubber's Close.

"You know, a funny thing about you, Wattie," said Will, "you talk well, nobody can compare with you in telling a tale, you know an amazing amount about the oddest sort of things, and you have a memory that is positively portentous—and yet you seem to be quite unconscious of these gifts and you preen yourself excessively instead on your physical prowess!"

"Vanity and hope, as Mrs. Cockburn says, are the great enliveners of life."

"I've no quarrel with your vanity. But you choose such odd things to be vain about!"

It was true. Walter was silent, thinking how puffed up he had been a few days before when Will's midshipman brother had introduced him to a group of his sailor friends, saying, "As for Mr. Scott, you may take him for a poor lamiter, but he is the first to begin a row and the last to end it." It went back, he thought, to his childhood, when he had resolved to make his place among the other lads in spite of his lame leg, asking no favors because of it. He had done it. It was a measure of his success that Will Clerk could say what he had just said without giving a thought to the reason behind it.

His lameness didn't matter any more. He started even with everybody else.

27

HERCULES AND
GREEN MANTLE

W ALTER was wandering after church among the
gravestones in Greyfriars kirkyard. It was going to
rain in rather less than half a second, he thought. The
Castle, a gray wraith up in the sky, was already being
blotted out by the shower, and at his feet a harebell at
the edge of the path bent under the first heavy drop. He
opened his umbrella.

He never came among these old graves without thinking of the Covenanters and Montrose. Montrose sign-
ing his name with theirs on the flat-topped stone, and
afterwards recanting. It was never fear that made him
recant, it was sincere belief, for which he later gave his
life with as magnificent courage as any of them. But before that, how must he have felt when he heard they
were imprisoned, beaten, starved, suffering, in the very
graveyard in which he too had signed the Covenant! And
what a story it would make!

Stragglers were still coming out of church, uttering

sounds of dismay when they saw the rain coming down. He saw the Countess of Sutherland and her husband run down the path and get into their waiting carriage. They were stopping in Edinburgh on their way to Dunrobin, Lady Elizabeth's estate in the North. Walter had talked with Lady Elizabeth last night for the first time since her marriage. She looked, he thought, exactly as she always had, but she declared that she would never have known him.

"I remember a little, pale lad," she cried, "and you have grown big, and strong, and red-cheeked! Why, you're a young Hercules!"

Ladies, he thought, had a charming gift of exaggeration. Perhaps that was one reason why Will and Adam and the rest were suddenly so interested in the fair sex. They rallied him for being cold.

The rain was pelting now. He had better go home.

In the shelter of the portico a girl was standing, looking up anxiously at the sky. She was a very young girl, and she wore a green mantle. She seemed to be alone, and there were no carriages for hire on Sunday. She had no umbrella.

"May I escort you home under my umbrella?" he offered.

"Oh, I didn't see you. Thank you very much."

For an instant she turned her face up to him and smiled. A high-bred little face it was, framed in brown curls. Blue eyes he saw, with black lashes, a lovely skin with quick color. She put her hand on his arm, and after that he saw only her profile, half hidden by the green

hood that was fastened at her throat by a gold clasp set
with a sapphire.

Her little morocco-shod feet picked their way daintily
over the wet paving stones; her little gloved hand lay like
a leaf on his arm; her green mantle was of silk, embroidered, and its hood hid all of her face but a slender chin,
deliciously tilted, a pair of red lips, and the merest tip
of a nose.

Not much of a girl to see—but enough to fall forever
in love with.

NOTE

Certain of the persons in this book were the originals of characters in Sir Walter Scott's novels, as follows:

WALTER SCOTT: Alan Fairford, in *Redgauntlet*.

MR. SCOTT: Saunders Fairford, in *Redgauntlet*, and, to a certain extent, William Osbaldistone, in *Rob Roy*.

MR. ALASTER STEWART of Invernahyle: The Baron of Bradwardine, in *Waverley*.

MR. GEORGE CONSTABLE: Jonathan Oldbuck of Monk-barns, in *The Antiquary*.

LANCELOT WHALE: Dominie Sampson, in *Guy Mannering*.

LADY WALDIE: Rachel Geddes, in *Redgauntlet*.

ANDREW GEMMELS: Edie Ochiltree, in *The Antiquary*.

WILL CLERK: Darsie Latimer, in *Redgauntlet*.

WILLIAMINA STUART of the green mantle: Matilda, in *Rokeby;* Margaret of Branksome, in *The Lay of the Last Minstrel;* and Green Mantle, in *Redgauntlet*.

LORD BRAXFIELD was the original of Lord Hermiston, in Robert Louis Stevenson's *Weir of Hermiston*.